Example

Questions highlight important ideas or are typical questions.

- -

Answers show how to apply appropriate techniques and layout your workings.

Each chapter also includes an Investigation section which provides a wider context and further directions in which to explore the material covered in the chapter. Opportunities to carry out research and investigate the use of ICT are highlighted. Each investigation also includes a suggestion for a project.

Project

An idea or a scenario which is designed to allow the material covered in the chapter to be developed into an extended activity.

At A2, Use of Mathematics contains a compulsory module, USE2, consisting of two projects. It is hoped that the ideas contained in the Investigation section may provide a useful springboard for any future studies.

The end of each chapter consists of two parts: a check out and consolidation questions. Some of the questions, and their mark allocations, are taken from actual past papers.

Check out

Summarises skills you should now be able to demonstrate having completed this chapter.

Each chapter makes use of information on data sheets which are included after the main chapters.

The book includes two realistic practice papers and their data sheets.

Answers for all questions are provided.

You are expected to use a graphical or scientific calculator in the examination. You should be able to use it to do basic calculations, including using function keys and the memory, and to draw graphs of functions and find the coordinates of significant points on the graph.

1 Linear functions

A **function** can be thought of as a rule for working out one variable from another. For example, the distance a car travels as a function of the time it has been travelling or the profit made by a car manufacturer as a function of the number of cars sold. A function is usually written as a formula or equation, such as $y = 5x + 4$. This is a **linear function**, so called because on a graph it gives a straight line.

Using functions and graphs to represent real life situations is known as **mathematical modelling**. In a simple model your height on a flight of steps as a function of the distance along the ground can be modelled by a straight line. The steepness of the line, or gradient, is given by the step's rise divided by its tread. Building regulations place limits on the gradient's values. By law the gradient of new stairs must be less than 0.9

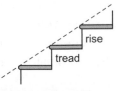

► Linear functions are used to model situations in many areas including, business, economics and physics

Before you start this chapter, you should be able to

- **Simplify algebraic expressions**

1 Expand and simplify **a)** $5(2x + 3) + 2(6x - 1)$
   b) $3(x - 4) - 4(3x - 5)$ **c)** $-2(3x + 4y) - 3(5 - 2x + 2y)$

- **Rearrange equations and formulae**

2 Make y the subject of the equation $3x + 2y = 6$

3 Make y the subject of the equation $\dfrac{2x - y}{4} = 5$

- **Plot coordinates in all four quadrants**

4 **a)** Plot the following points:
      A$(-3, 0)$; B$(-1, 2)$; C$(2, 2)$; D$(-1, 0)$; E$(1, -2)$; F$(-3, -3)$

   b) Connect them up with straight lines in the order EDFABCD.

- **Complete a table of data from a formula or equation**

5 Complete the table given that $2x + y = 5$

x	−2	0	2	4
y				

6 Plot the points with (x, y) coordinates from the table in question **5**, and join them with straight lines. Comment on your result.

Challenge

Look at **Vintage clothing** *on Data Sheet 1*

Anita and Seth want to buy between 100 kg and 300 kg of mixed-grade vintage clothing. They will choose between three suppliers: *Peppers*, *Funny Valentines* and *Tramps*. The quality of the clothes is similar at each supplier.

The table shows the cost per kilogram and the delivery charge for each supplier.

Supplier	Cost per kg	Delivery charge
Peppers	£2.25	£30
Funny Valentines	£2.40	free
Tramps	£2.20	£42

How would you decide which supplier to use?

1.1 Direct proportion and straight lines

Two variables y and x are directly proportional if
$$y = \text{(a fixed number)} \times x$$
This fixed number is called the **constant of proportionality**.

> ▶ If y and x are directly proportional,
> $$y = kx$$
>   where k is the constant of proportionality

> ▶ $y \propto x$ means 'y is directly proportional to x'

An example of a pair of variables which are directly proportional is
   number of cans of drink and *total cost.*

If a can of drink costs 65 pence, and I pay C pence for n cans, then
   $$C = 65n$$
You multiply one variable by a constant, k, to find the other variable.
In this case $k = 65$.

> ▶ An easy way of telling if two quantities are **directly proportional** is
>   if one amount doubles the other will also double

Example 1

The number of horses in a field is directly proportional to the area of the field in hectares.
A field of area 12 hectares contains 18 horses.
a) How many horses are in a field of 10 hectares?
b) What is the area of a field containing 21 horses?

- -

Let A = area of field in hectares
Let N = number of horses
Then $N = kA$

That is, $18 = 12k \implies k = 18 \div 12 = 1.5$

So $N = 1.5A$

a) $N = 1.5 \times 10 = 15$ **b)** $A = 21 \div 1.5 = 14$

> The key is to find the constant of proportionality k.

> ▶ A graph showing direct proportion is a straight line through the origin

The graph shows the cost £y of x kg of mixed-grade vintage clothing.
As you can see, the graph goes up 2.5 units for every 1 unit it goes across.
Clearly, the clothes cost £2.50 per kilo.
So $k = 2.5$ and the equation connecting y and x is $y - 2.5x$

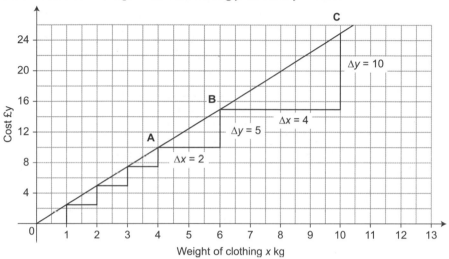

> ▶ The **gradient**, m, of a straight line graph is defined as $m = \dfrac{\Delta y}{\Delta x}$
> where Δx means 'change in x' and Δy means 'change in y'

In this case you can see that between

    the points A and B, $\Delta x = 2$ and $\Delta y = 5$,   so $\dfrac{\Delta y}{\Delta x} = \dfrac{5}{2} = 2.5$

    the points B and C, $\Delta x = 4$ and $\Delta y = 10$,   so $\dfrac{\Delta y}{\Delta x} = \dfrac{10}{4} = 2.5$

Whichever two points you choose you will always get $m = 2.5$

> ▶ The units of the gradient are (units of y) per (unit of x)

In this case the units are £ per kg

> ▶ In a graph showing direct proportion, the gradient m is equal to the
> constant of proportionality k, $m = k$

7

Look back at the graph on page 7. Suppose the supplier decides to add a fixed delivery charge of £6 to every order.

The equation now becomes $y = 2.5x + 6$

The effect on the graph is to move it up by 6 units. So the graph no longer shows direct proportion, as it does not go through the origin.

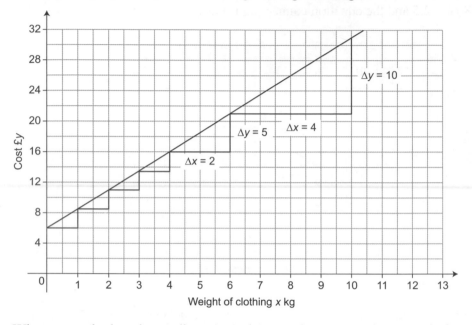

When you calculate the gradient, Δx and Δy are the same as they were before. So the gradient is still 2.5

▶ The y-intercept, c, of the graph is the point where it crosses the y-axis

c is often just called the **intercept**.

Here the intercept is $c = 6$.

▶ The equation of a straight line can be written in the form
$y = mx + c$
where m is the gradient and c is the intercept.

A graph that goes downhill from left to right has a **negative gradient**.

You can think of Δx as positive and Δy as negative.

For example, this graph shows the amount of water y litres in a bath at a time x seconds after it starts emptying.

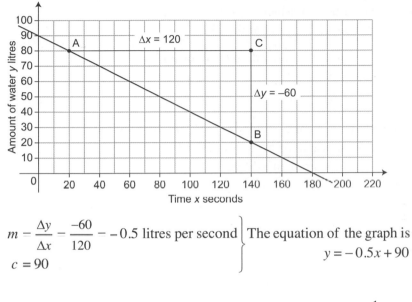

$m = \dfrac{\Delta y}{\Delta x} = \dfrac{-60}{120} = -0.5$ litres per second

$c = 90$

The equation of the graph is
$$y = -0.5x + 90$$

This equation can be written in other ways, such as $\quad y = 90 - \dfrac{1}{2}x$

or $\quad 2y + x = 180$

Example 2

Find the gradient and intercept of each of the following lines

a) $y = 5x - 4$ **b)** $y = 6 - x$ **c)** $3x + 2y = 14$

- -

a) Compare with the standard equation $y = mx + c$
$m = 5$ and $c = -4$

b) Rewrite as $y = -1 \times x + 6$
$m = -1$ and $c = 6$

c) Rearrange the equation to make y the subject
$3x + 2y = 14$
$\quad 2y = -3x + 14$
$\quad\quad y = -1.5x + 7$
$m = -1.5$ and $c = 7$

9

Exercise 1.1

1 The amount, £y, paid for fish is directly proportional to the weight, x kg.
6 kg of fish cost £81.
   a) Find an expression for y in terms of x
   b) What is the value of y when $x = 4.2$?
   c) How much fish would you get for £32?

2 Which of these equations show direct proportion?
   a) $y = 0.5x$ b) $y = 3x + 1$ c) $y = x$
   d) $y = x - 5$ e) $y = 2$ f) $y = -3x$

3 The graph shows the cost, y Swiss Francs, of x litres of fuel.
   a) Estimate the constant of proportionality k
      i) by finding the gradient of OA
      ii) by finding the gradient of OB.
   b) Which gives a more accurate value? Why do you think this is?

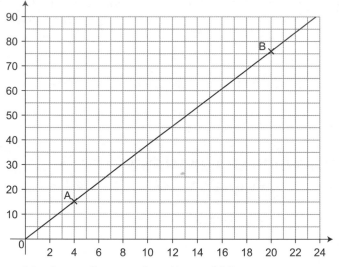

4 The table shows distances in miles and kilometres.

Distance in miles x	10	20	30	40
Distance in kilometres y	16	32	48	64

   a) What is the equation in the form $y = ...$?
   b) What is the equation in the form $x = ...$?
   c) What is the connection between the constants in a) and b)?

5 Set up a currency converter graph on a spreadsheet. Find buying and selling rates online, and draw two graphs on the same axes.

6 Find the gradient of each of these lines.

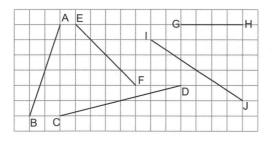

Take each square to be one unit by one unit.

7 Find the gradient and intercept of each of these lines.
a) $y = 8x + 3$ **b)** $y = 6 - 4x$
c) $7x + y = 5$ **d)** $5x - 4y - 6 = 0$

8 If $x + 2y = 20$
a) Find y when $x - 0$ **b)** Find x when $y - 0$
c) Use these results to *sketch* the graph of $x + 2y = 20$
d) What is the gradient of the graph?

9 For each of these graphs find the values shown at A, B and C.
a) Hire of a floor sander costs £12 per day plus a fixed charge of £5.

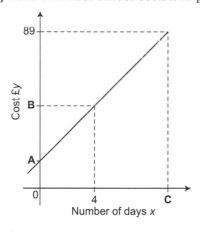

b) The air temperature is –8 °C at 06: 00.
It then increases steadily by 2 °C every hour until 16: 00.

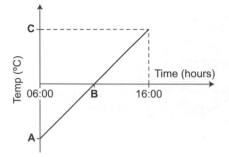

c) An underground train has an initial speed of 12 metres per second (m/s).
It then slows down by 1.5 m/s every second until it stops.

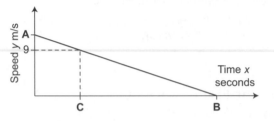

10 a) Find the equation of each of the graphs in question **9**.
b) State the units of the gradient for each of the graphs in question **9**.

11 Use a graphics package or calculator to investigate graphs of the
form x = constant or y = constant, for example, $x = -2$ or $y = 3$.
How can you describe the shape of these graphs?
What can you say about their gradients?

12 Find the equation of each of these lines.

> **Hint:** find m and c.

a)

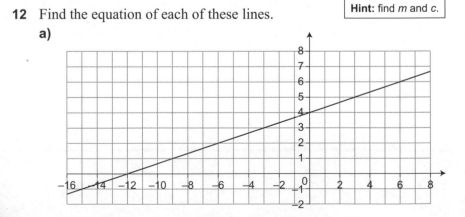

b)

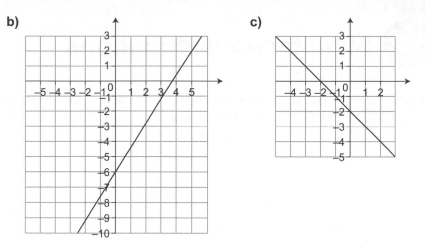

c)

13 If you know the coordinates of two points P and Q on a line, there is a formula you can use to find the gradient of the line.

If point P has coordinates (x_1, y_1) and Q is (x_2, y_2) then

$$m = \frac{\Delta y}{\Delta x} = \frac{y_2 - y_1}{x_2 - x_1}$$

Use this formula to find the gradient of the line PQ in these cases.

a) P(3, 8) and Q(5, 1)   **b)** P(−9, 5) and Q(−6, 15)
c) P(0, −5) and Q(−4, 11)   **d)** P(−2, 3) and Q(−4, −5)

Check your answers by drawing by hand, computer or calculator.

14 It is also possible to find the intercept using algebra.

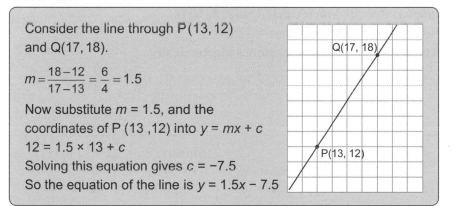

Consider the line through P(13, 12) and Q(17, 18).

$$m = \frac{18 - 12}{17 - 13} = \frac{6}{4} = 1.5$$

Now substitute $m = 1.5$, and the coordinates of P (13, 12) into $y = mx + c$

$12 = 1.5 \times 13 + c$

Solving this equation gives $c = -7.5$

So the equation of the line is $y = 1.5x - 7.5$

Use this method to find the equation of the line through P(11, 27) and Q(19, 3).

1.2 Simultaneous equations

p.5

Suppose that Seth and Anita (see **Challenge**) want to decide whether to use *Funny Valentines* or *Tramps*. For small amounts, *Funny Valentines* will be cheaper, as there is no delivery charge. How much clothing will they have to buy before *Tramps* becomes the cheaper option?

You can write equations to model each option.

Let x kg be the amount of clothing and £y be the cost.
Then for *Funny Valentines* $y = 2.4x$ and   for *Tramps* $y = 2.2x + 42$

You can **draw graphs** of these two functions on the same axes. If you were drawing the graphs by hand you would use a table.

x	0	100	200	300
y = 2.4x	0	240	480	720
y = 2.2x + 42	42	262	482	702

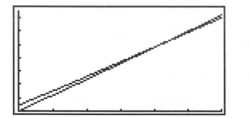
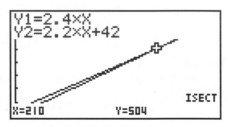

If you use a computer or calculator, you can zoom in to point A, where the graphs intersect. You see that A is (210, 504).
So *Tramps* is cheaper when $x > 210$.
You could also solve the equations **algebraically**.
Where the graphs meet, $y = 2.4x$ So $2.4x = 2.2x + 42$
                     and $y = 2.2x + 42$ $0.2x = 42$

$$x = \frac{42}{0.2} = 210$$

Example 3

Solve the simultaneous equations
(1) $2x + 3y = 4$ (2) $y = 2x - 12$

> Include both x and y in your answer, and state which is which.

Substitute $y = 2x - 12$ in (1)
$2x + 3(2x - 12) = 4$
$2x + 6x - 36 = 4$
$8x = 40$ $\Rightarrow$ $x = 5$
and $y = 2 \times 5 - 12 = -2$
Check in (1): $2 \times 5 + 3 \times -2 = 4$ ✔

Simultaneous equations can also be solved by the method of **elimination**.

Amy and Ben buy some musical accessories for their guitars.

Given the following information, what is the price of a set of strings and the price of a lead?

5 sets of strings and 2 leads cost £50
3 sets of strings and 2 leads cost £38

Find the difference:
2 sets of strings cost £12.
So 1 set of strings costs £6.
3 sets of strings cost £18.
So 2 leads cost £38 – £18 = £20
and 1 lead costs £10.

> *The same calculation in algebra*
> Let £x = cost of strings
> Let £y = cost of a lead
> $$5x + 2y = 50 \qquad (1)$$
> $$3x + 2y = 38 \qquad (2)$$
>
> $(1) - (2) \quad 2x = 12$
> $\qquad\qquad\qquad x = 6$
> Subst. in (2) $\quad 3 \times 6 + 2y = 38$
> $\qquad\qquad\qquad\qquad 2y = 20$
> $\qquad\qquad\qquad\qquad y = 10$
> Check in (1)
> $5 \times 6 + 2 \times 10 = 50$ ✔

This worked easily because the number of leads, the term $2y$, was the same in each equation, meaning that when you subtracted y was eliminated.

► If there is no unknown with the same coefficient in both equations you have to multiply one or both equations by a suitable number

Example 4
3 pizzas and 8 pasta dishes cost £74
2 pizzas and 5 pasta dishes cost £47
Find the cost of:
a) a pizza   **b)** a pasta dish.

6 pizzas and 16 pasta dishes cost £148.

Multiply each equation by a different number so that the terms in x (or the terms in y) are equal.

Let £x be the cost of a pizza.
Let £y be the cost of a pasta.
$$3x + 8y = 74 \qquad (1)$$
$$2x + 5y = 47 \qquad (2)$$
$2 \times (1) \quad 6x + 16y = 148 \quad (3)$
$3 \times (2) \quad 6x + 15y = 141 \quad (4)$
$(3) - (4) \qquad\qquad y = 7$

A pasta dish costs £7
Subst. in (1): $\quad 3x + 8 \times 7 = 74$
$\qquad\qquad\qquad\qquad x = 6$

A pizza costs £6
Check in (2): $2 \times 6 + 5 \times 7 = 47$ ✔

Exercise 1.2

1 Solve the following pairs of simultaneous equations graphically.

a) $y = 8x + 4$

$\quad y = 12x - 10$

b) $y = 3x + 2$

$\quad 2y + 5x = 20$

2 Solve the following pairs of simultaneous equations by substitution.

a) $y = 0.5x - 18$

$\quad y = 12 - 2x$

b) $y = 4x - 7$

$\quad 12x - 2y = 32$

3 Solve the following pairs of simultaneous equations by elimination.

a) $4x + 3y = 5$

$\quad x + 3y = 17$

b) $5x + 2y = 11$

$\quad 5x - y = 2$

c) $8x - 2y = 16$

$\quad 8x - 5y = 4$

d) $3x + 2y = 17$

$\quad 5x - 2y = 23$

e) $2x - 3y = 20$

$\quad 5x + 6y = 23$

f) $2x + 5y = 2$

$\quad 3x - 4y = 49$

4 Look at the **Challenge** on page 5 again.

a) Write an equation for the cost of buying from *Peppers*.

b) Draw the graphs for *Peppers*, *Funny Valentines* and *Tramps* on the same axes (you may use a computer or calculator).

c) Use an algebraic method to

  i) solve simultaneously the equations for *Peppers* and *Funny Valentines*

  ii) solve simultaneously the equations for *Peppers* and *Tramps*.

d) Use your answers to **b)** and **c)** to work out the range of values of x for which each option is the cheapest.

5 Two taxi firms, *Yellow Cabs* and *Transcars*, each have a fixed charge plus a charge per mile, as shown in the table.

Firm	Fixed charge	Charge per mile
Yellow Cabs	£4	70p
Transcars	£2.50	90p

a) Write equations for the cost of using each firm.

b) Solve your equations simultaneously.

c) Interpret your answer to **b)**.

6 A factory produces x T-shirts in a period of one week, at a cost of £P.
The costs of production consist of a fixed cost and a cost per T-shirt.
$P = 3.2x + 1500$

   a) How much is the fixed cost?
   b) What is the gradient of the graph of $P = 3.2x + 1500$?
   c) What are the units of the gradient?

   The income £I from the sale of the T-shirts is given by $I = 5.5x$

   d) Draw the graphs of P and I on the same axes.
   e) Find the value of x for which the production costs and income are
   equal. This is called the break-even point.

7 4 cans of cola and 5 packets of crisps cost £3.50
11 cans of cola and 8 packets of crisps cost £6.98
Write down two simultaneous equations and solve
them by elimination to find the cost of each item.

> Define what x and y
> stand for before you
> start.

8 A toy company makes two items in its factory, aliens and bears.
The same eyes and the same limbs are used in each item.
An alien has one eye and five limbs.
A bear has two eyes and four limbs.

The factory director has 2000 toy eyes and 6400 toy limbs available.
She wants to use all these eyes and limbs to make aliens and bears.

   a) Write two equations, one for the eyes and one for the limbs.
   Define what your letters stand for.
   b) Solve the equations simultaneously.
   c) Interpret your answer to **b)**.

1.3 Line of best fit

Sometimes using a linear model will give us useful results, even if the model is not completely accurate.

Suppose a cafe owner keeps a record of the number of cups of hot chocolate sold and the maximum daily temperature, as shown in the table.

Temperature (°C)	2	4	6	9	11	17	18	20	23
Number of hot chocolates sold	32	34	30	23	23	15	12	8	2

When you plot these data, you see that the points do not lie exactly on a straight line. But you can draw a line which goes close to all the points, with about the same number of points above and below the line. This is a **line of best fit**.

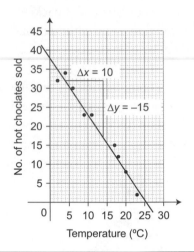

The module Data Analysis discusses in more detail finding lines of best fit.

Example 5

a) Find the equation of the line of best fit drawn above.

b) Use your equation to estimate the likely number of hot chocolates sold when the temperature is 14°C.

c) Explain why this model would not be suitable for predicting the likely number of hot chocolates sold when the temperature is 27°C.

- -

a) $m = \dfrac{-15}{10} = -1.5$ and $c = 38$,

the equation is $y = -1.5x + 38$

Confirm this by checking the graph.

b) $-1.5 \times 14 + 38 = 17$ hot chocolates.

c) The number of hot chocolates sold would be negative.

Exercise 1.3

1 A number of women do aerobics for one minute.
Their ages and heart rates after the exercise are shown in the table.

Age (years)	16	17	22	25	38	42	43	50
Heart rate (beats per minute)	82	78	83	90	99	97	108	107

a) Draw a graph of this data and draw a line of best fit on your graph.

b) Betty is 35 years old. Use your line of best fit to estimate her heart rate after doing aerobics for one minute.

2 The graph shows the amount invested in one year and the profit in that year for five companies, together with a line of best fit.

a) Find the equation of the line of best fit.

b) Use your equation to predict the profit for a company with investment £5 million.

c) Explain what the model predicts when the investment is less than £1 million.

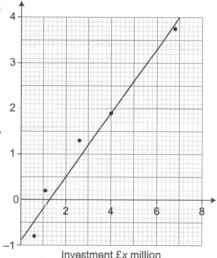

Investment £x million

3 The table shows the cost in Euros of a small bottle of water and the distance from a museum to the shop where the water was sold.

Distance, x km	0.04	0.16	0.3	0.38	0.4	0.46	0.6	0.72
Cost of bottle, €y	1.60	1.20	1.00	1.00	1.20	0.80	0.60	0.65

a) Draw a graph of this data and draw a line of best fit on your graph.

b) Find the equation of the line of best fit.

c) Use your equation to predict the cost of a bottle of water 0.5 km from the museum.

Investigation – Linear functions

Linear programming is a powerful method for working out how to make the best use of limited resources. Restrictions on resources are expressed by **linear inequalities**. Algorithms such as the *simplex method* can then be used to find an optimal solution for situations with hundreds or thousands of constraints.

ICT opportunity

Use a graphics package to investigate how to show linear inequalities by shading regions on a graph.

You can get an idea of the methods involved by writing down a small number of inequalities and showing them on a graph.

The unshaded region here shows the set of values of x and y that satisfy the inequality $y \geq 2x - 3$.

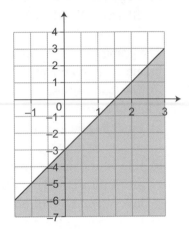

1 Show, by leaving it *unshaded* on a graph, the region where all of the following inequalities are satisfied.
$$x \geq 0$$
$$y \geq 0$$
$$x + 2y \leq 4 \text{ and}$$
$$6x + 4y \leq 12$$

Leonid Kantorovich, who developed the simplex method, was born in St Petersburg in 1912. A gifted mathematician, he completed his PhD at the age of 18!

In 1938 he acted as a consultant to the USSR Plywood Trust on a problem of distributing raw materials in order to maximise productivity. He used his mathematical knowledge to find an efficient method of solving this problem, and many similar ones, using the simplex method.

He was awarded the Nobel Prize for Economics in 1975, jointly with Tjalling Koopmans.

Look back at Exercise **1.2**, Q.**8**. Use the same information about the number of eyes and limbs but this time assume that there are 1000 eyes and 3800 limbs available. If you make x aliens and y bears, then x and y must satisfy the following inequalities.

$$x \geq 0$$
$$y \geq 0$$
$$x + 2y \leq 1000$$

Research

Find out more about linear programming. Linear programming is a technique for solving a type of optimization problem. Find examples of problems where you have to maximize a function.

2 a) Write down another inequality that x and y must satisfy.

> A region satisfying all the inequalities is known as the **feasible region**.

b) Draw a graph showing the region that satisfies all four inequalities.

Now, instead of necessarily using all the eyes and limbs, you can try to maximise profits. Assume that you make £9 profit on an alien and £6 profit on a bear. Linear programming theory tells us that profit will be maximised at a **vertex**, that is, a corner of the feasible region.

3 a) If P is the total profit made, find an expression for P in terms of x and y.

> A function that you try to maximise or minimise is known as an **objective function**.

b) Find the value of P at each vertex of the feasible region.
State how many bears and how many aliens you need to make in order to maximise the profit.

c) Using the same feasible region, now assume that you make £8 profit on an alien and £8 profit on a bear. Test each vertex again to see what numbers of aliens and bears produce the most profit.

Project

Investigate a situation where resources are limited and these constraints can be expressed as linear inequalities.

Look for a way of maximising or minimising an objective function such as profit without having to evaluate it at every vertex of the feasible region. This saves time when you have a large number of constraints.

Consolidation

You should now be able to
- Solve problems involving direct proportion
- Find gradients, intercepts and equations of straight lines
- Model real-life situations using straight-line graphs and equations
- Solve simultaneous equations graphically
- Solve simultaneous equations algebraically by substitution or elimination
- Model real-life situations using simultaneous equations
- Draw lines of best fit and use them to predict values
- Interpret the results of your calculations

1 Use *Babies* on Data Sheet **1**
   a) Plot the data pairs on a graph, and draw a line of best fit.   (*3 marks*)
   b) Use your line of best fit to predict the weight of a
      baby aged 8 weeks.   (*1 mark*)
   c) Find the gradient of your graph.   (*2 marks*)
   d) State the units of the gradient.   (*1 mark*)
   e) Give a practical interpretation of your answer to **c)**.   (*1 mark*)
                                                                       (AQA 2007)

2 Use *Plumbers* on Data Sheet **1**
   The table below shows the amount charged for labour by a plumber.

Hours worked, x	2	3.5	5	7.5
Amount charged, £y	92	131	170	235

   a) Plot the data pairs on a graph, and join them with
      a straight line.   (*2 marks*)
   b) Find the equation of your line.   (*2 marks*)

3   Use *Plumbers* on Data Sheet **1**
    PM Plumbers charge for labour using the equation $y = 30x + 35$
    a) How much is the fixed callout charge?   (*1 mark*)
    b) How much is the charge per hour?   (*1 mark*)
    Tapsters plumbers have a fixed callout charge of £50
    with a further charge of £24 per hour for labour.
    c) Write down an equation in the form $y = ax + b$ for
        the total amount charged by *Tapsters*.   (*1 mark*)
    d) Solve simultaneously the equation $y = 30x + 35$
        and the equation which was your answer to **c)**.   (*3 marks*)
    e) Give a practical interpretation of your answer to **d)**.   (*1 mark*)

Use *Fuel consumption* on Data Sheet **1**
4   The mass, x kg, of each of ten cars is shown on the Data Sheet,
    with the car's average fuel consumption, y miles per gallon.
    A graph of the data is shown below.

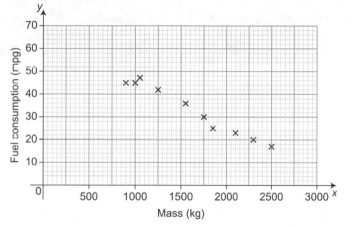

A line of best fit is given by the equation $y = 65.2 - 0.0199x$

    a) On a copy of the graph, draw the line $y = 65.2 - 0.0199x$. (*3 marks*)
    b) What is the gradient of this line?   (*1 mark*)
    c) Use the line to predict the average fuel consumption
        of a car of mass 1450 kg.   (*1 mark*)
    d) Cars that have a small mass can have an average fuel
        consumption of over 70 mpg.
        Why is the above line of best fit not appropriate
        for these cars?   (*1 mark*)
                                                                        (AQA 2010)

Quadratic functions

The **parabola** is the shape of the cross-section that you obtain when you slice through a cone parallel to its edge. Its properties have been extensively studied by mathematicians since the time of the ancient Greeks.

The parabola has several useful geometric properties. If a parabola is rotated about its axis of symmetry to make a bowl shape, then beams of light hitting the bowl parallel to the axis will all be reflected to focus on a single point. This makes it an ideal shape for satellite dishes and solar cookers.

The equation of a parabola is given by a quadratic function.

> ▶ A **quadratic function** has the form $y = ax^2 + bx + c$, where a, b, and c are constants and $a \neq 0$

A function with highest power x^3 or x^4 is called a cubic or quartic function.

Quadratic functions are used to model a wide range of shapes. They describe the trajectory of a projectile when only gravity acts on it, the stopping distances of cars and the shape of a suspension bridge that carries a uniform load.

The shape of the Millennium Bridge on the cover of this book is a parabola.

Quadratic function also provide useful first approximations to other more complex functions and so find widespread use in other subjects such as economics, physics and chemistry.

▶ Quadratic functions have many real world applications

Preparation

Before you start this chapter, you should be able to

■ **Expand, factorise and simplify expressions**

1 Expand out these double brackets.
   a) $(x + 2)(x + 6)$ **b)** $(x - 4)(x + 9)$ **c)** $(x - 5)(x + 5)$
   d) $(x - 1)(x - 8)$ **e)** $(x - 3)^2$ **f)** $(4x + 1)(3x - 5)$

2 Factorise these expressions with two terms.
   a) $3x - 6$ **b)** $x^2 + 9x$ **c)** $4x^2 - 10x$

3 Expand and simplify these expressions.
   a) $(x - 4)^2 + 5x - 6$ **b)** $8(x + 3)^2 - 27$
   c) $-(x - 7)^2 + 31$ **d)** $(2x + 3)(x - 7) + 3x + 9$

■ **Complete tables and draw graphs of quadratic functions**

4 Complete a copy of the table for
   $y = 0.5x^2 - 4x + 7$
   and draw the graph of y against x.

x	0	2	4	6	8
y		1			

Challenge

Look at **Skateboard Ramps** *on Data Sheet* **2**

Errol and Ji are designing some skateboard ramps. The cross-sectional shape of their ramps is to be based on the parabola, $y = x^2$ where x is the horizontal and y the vertical distance from a fixed point (the origin).

They want to have ramps to the left and right of their origin and at different heights, as well as having ramps which are more or less steep. They are even considering having an upside down ramp.

You have been asked by Errol and Ji to find suitable equations to accurately model their ramps which they can then use to create virtual versions for use in an online game.

2.1 Factorisation

A fielder throws a cricket ball to the wicket-keeper. The path of the ball through the air can be modelled by the equation $y = x - \frac{1}{40}x^2$ where x metres is the horizontal distance and y metres is the vertical height, both measured from the point from where the ball was thrown.

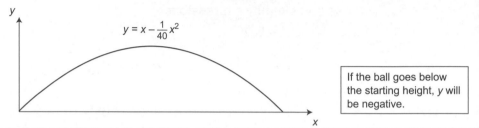

$y = x - \frac{1}{40}x^2$

> If the ball goes below the starting height, y will be negative.

If the wicket-keeper catches the ball at the same height as it was thrown from, what horizontal distance does it travel?

When the wicket-keeper catches the ball, $y = 0$

$$x - \frac{1}{40}x^2 = 0$$

> If two numbers multiply to make zero, at least one of them must be zero.

Factorising, $\quad x\left(1 - \frac{1}{40}x\right) = 0$

$$x = 0 \quad \text{or} \quad 1 - \frac{1}{40}x = 0$$

$$\text{giving} \quad x = 40$$

Since $x = 0$ is the starting point, you want the other solution. The horizontal distance travelled is 40 metres.

This equation is quite easy to factorise because it has only an x^2-term and an x-term. To factorise a quadratic expression or equation with three terms, such as $x^2 + 7x + 10 = 0$, you need to consider the reverse process, expanding double brackets.

For example $(x + 2)(x + 5) \equiv x^2 + 2x + 5x + 10$
$$\equiv x^2 + 7x + 10$$

> The $\equiv$ sign is used to emphasise that this is an **identity**. That is, it is true for all values of x.

▶ To factorise $x^2 + bx + c$, you need to find two numbers which add up to give b and which multiply together to give c

Since $2 + 5 = 7$ and $2 \times 5 = 10$
$$x^2 + 7x + 10 \equiv (x + 2)(x + 5)$$

If $x^2 + 7x + 10 = 0$ then $(x + 2)(x + 5) = 0$

$\Rightarrow \qquad x + 2 = 0 \quad$ or $\qquad\qquad x + 5 = 0$

$\qquad\qquad\quad x = -2 \qquad\qquad\qquad\qquad x = -5$

> ▶ If you want to solve the equation $x^2 + (p + q)x + pq = 0$
> you can factorise the left hand side $(x + p)(x + q) = 0$

Example 1

Use factorisation to solve the equations

a) $x^2 + 12x + 27 = 0$ **b)** $x^2 + 3x - 40 = 0$

- -

a) $(x + 3)(x + 9) = 0$

$\quad x + 3 = 0 \quad$ or $\quad x + 9 = 0$

$\qquad x = -3 \quad$ or $\qquad x = -9$

$\boxed{3 + 9 = 12 \text{ and } 3 \times 9 = 27}$

b) $(x + 8)(x - 5) = 0$

$\quad x + 8 = 0 \quad$ or $\quad x - 5 = 0$

$\qquad x = -8 \quad$ or $\qquad x = 5$

$\boxed{8 + -5 = 3 \text{ and } 8 \times -5 = -40}$

Not all quadratic expressions can be factorised, but if you can factorise an expression it is often a quick way to solve an equation or sketch a curve.

Example 2

Factorise the following quadratic expressions where possible.

a) $x^2 - 20x + 64$ **b)** $x^2 + 9x$ **c)** $x^2 + 25$

d) $x^2 - 36$ **e)** $x^2 + 2x - 11$ **f)** $9x^2 + 30x + 25$

- -

a) $x^2 - 20x + 64 \equiv (x - 16)(x - 4)$

$\boxed{\begin{array}{l} -4 + -16 = -20 \text{ and} \\ -4 \times -16 = 64 \end{array}}$

b) $x^2 + 9x \equiv x(x + 9)$

c) $x^2 + 25$ cannot be factorised

$\boxed{x^2 + 25 = 0 \text{ has no solutions}}$ p.34

d) $x^2 - 36 \equiv (x - 6)(x + 6)$

$\boxed{\begin{array}{l} \text{Difference of two squares:} \\ x^2 - a^2 \equiv (x - a)(x + a) \end{array}}$

e) $x^2 + 2x - 11$ cannot be factorised

$\boxed{\begin{array}{l} \text{It is still possible to solve the} \\ \text{equation } x^2 + 2x - 11 = 0 \end{array}}$ p.34

f) $9x^2 + 30x + 25 \equiv (3x + 5)^2$

$\boxed{\begin{array}{l} \text{Perfect square:} \\ (a + b)^2 \equiv a^2 + 2ab + b^2 \end{array}}$

Exercise 2.1

1 Expand these expressions.

   a) $(2x + 5)(2x - 5)$ **b)** $(7x + 3y)(7x - 3y)$ **c)** $(4x + 5)^2$

   d) $(10q - 3)^2$ **e)** $8x(5x - 12)$ **f)** $y^2(3y + 9)$

   g) $-4x(x + 6)^2$ **h)** $x(x + 3)(x - 3)$ **i)** $T(T + 7)(T - 5)$

2 Factorise these expressions.

   a) $x^2 + 11x + 28$ **b)** $T^2 - T - 12$ **c)** $x^2 - 5x - 24$

   d) $x^2 + 5x - 24$ **e)** $y^2 - 11y + 30$ **f)** $6x^2 + 4x$

   g) $x^3 - x^2$ **h)** $t^2 - 64$ **i)** $15x^2 - 240$

   j) $9v^2 - 4$ **k)** $5x^2 + 20x + 15$ **l)** $x^3 - x$

   m) $w^2 + 12w + 36$ **n)** $4x^2 - 20x + 25$ **o)** $9x^3 + 24x^2 + 16x$

   p) $49 - w^2$ **q)** $15 + 2x - x^2$ **r)** $25 - 20x + 4x^2$

3 Solve these equations.

   a) $x(2x + 3) = 0$ **b)** $(x + 3)(2x - 1) = 0$

   c) $x^2 + 5x = 0$ **d)** $23t - t^2 = 0$

   e) $n^2 + 4n + 3 = 0$ **f)** $x^2 + 12x + 20 = 0$

   g) $N^2 - 9N + 14 = 0$ **h)** $x^2 + 12x - 28 = 0$

   i) $x^2 - x - 42 = 0$ **j)** $C^2 - 81 = 0$

   k) $6T^2 - 24 = 0$ **l)** $x^2 + 14x + 49 = 0$

   m) $x^2 - 18x + 81 = 0$ **n)** $4x^2 + 20x + 25 = 0$

   o) $4y^3 - 12y^2 = 0$ **p)** $x^3 - 4x^2 + 3x = 0$

> You can check your solutions by plotting the graph on a calculator or computer.

> Part **p)** has three solutions.

4 Rearrange and solve these equations.

   a) $x^2 + 5x = 6$

   b) $t^2 - 12 = 4t$

   c) $x^2 + x = 9x + 48$

   d) $(x - 4)^2 - 5x + 14 = 0$

   e) $x^2 - 13x + 5 = -3x - 16$

   f) $p + 8 = \dfrac{9}{p}$

> To check your answers to **4c)**, plot the graphs of $y = x^2 + x$ and $y = 9x + 48$ on the same axes. Look at the values of x where the graphs intersect.

> In part **f)** cross-multiply.

5   The cable of a suspension bridge is modelled by the equation

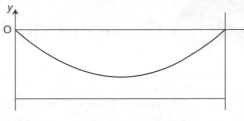

$y = 0.02x^2 - 1.2x$, where x metres is the horizontal distance and y metres is the height, measured from a fixed point O.

a) Find the distance from O where the cable is next at the same height as O.
b) Use the fact that the cable has a vertical axis of symmetry to find the horizontal distance from O where the cable is at its lowest point. p.38
c) Use your answer to **b)** to find the greatest depth of the cable below O.

6   A rocket is fired up into the air from ground level. Its flight is modelled by the equation $y = 3x(r - x)$, where r is a constant, x metres is the horizontal distance and y metres is the height, measured from its starting point O. The rocket hits the ground again at a distance of 20 m from O.

a) Write down the value of the constant r.
b) Write down an equation that x satisfies when the rocket is at a height of 252 m.
   Show that this equation simplifies to $x^2 - 20x + 84 = 0$.
c) Solve this equation to find the horizontal distances of the rocket from O when it is at a height of 252 m.

7   Use your calculator or computer application to investigate graphs of the following types of equation, where a, m and n are constants ($a > 0$).

a) $y = ax(x - m)$
b) $y = ax(m - x)$
c) $y = a(x - m)(x - n)$

Describe the effects of varying the constants a, m and n.

2.2 Completing the square

If you expand $(x + 5)^2$ you get $x^2 + 10x + 25$. Similarly $(x - 7)^2 \equiv x^2 - 14x + 49$.

▶ If you square a bracket containing x and a constant term, p, it follows this pattern: $\qquad (x + p)^2 \equiv x^2 + 2px + p^2$

Sometimes it is useful to reverse this process.
$$x^2 - 14x + 49 \equiv (x - 7)^2$$
Subtract 49 from each side $\qquad x^2 - 14x \equiv (x - 7)^2 - 49$
In the same way $\qquad\qquad\quad x^2 + 10x \equiv (x + 5)^2 - 25$

▶ In completing the square $x^2 + bx$ is expressed in the form $(x + p)^2 - p^2$ where $p = b \div 2$

Example 3

Express in the form $(x + p)^2 + q$

a) $x^2 + 22x$

b) $x^2 - 3x + 8$

---

a) $p = 22 \div 2 = 11$ and

$\qquad q = -p^2 = -121$

$\qquad x^2 + 22x \equiv (x + 11)^2 - 121$

b) Considering the first two terms

$\qquad p = -\dfrac{3}{2}, \quad p^2 = 2\dfrac{1}{4}$

$\qquad x^2 - 3x \equiv \left(x - \dfrac{3}{2}\right)^2 - 2\dfrac{1}{4}$

Adding 8 to both sides

$\qquad x^2 - 3x + 8 \equiv \left(x - \dfrac{3}{2}\right)^2 - 2\dfrac{1}{4} + 8$

$\qquad\qquad\qquad\quad = \left(x - \dfrac{3}{2}\right)^2 + 5\dfrac{3}{4}$

You can solve quadratic equations (even those that can't be factorised) by completing the square.

Example 4

Solve the equation $x^2 + 10x + 14 = 0$ by completing the square.

$x^2 + 10x + 14 \equiv (x + 5)^2 - 25 + 14 = (x + 5)^2 - 11$

$(x + 5)^2 - 11 = 0 \quad$ so $\quad (x + 5)^2 = 11$

$\qquad x + 5 = \sqrt{11} \qquad$ or $\quad x + 5 = -\sqrt{11}$

$\qquad\quad x = \sqrt{11} - 5 \quad$ or $\qquad x = -\sqrt{11} - 5$

> When taking square roots, include both the positive and negative options.

You can also find the maximum or minimum value of a quadratic function by completing the square.

Example 5

If $f(x) \equiv x^2 + 10x + 14$, find the minimum value of $f(x)$ and the value of x which gives that minimum value.

- -

From example **4**, $f(x) \equiv (x + 5)^2 - 11$
$(x + 5)^2 \geq 0$

Minimum value of $(x + 5)^2$ is 0,   when $x = -5$ | A number squared must be
Minimum value of $f(x)$ is -11,   when $x = -5$ | either positive or zero

---

You can extend this technique to expressions in the form $ax^2 + bx + c$, where the x^2 coefficient is not 1.

Example 6

If $f(x) \equiv 2x^2 + 10x + 7$
a) express $f(x)$ in the form $f(x) \equiv a(x + p)^2 + q$
b) find the maximum value of $f(x)$ and the value of x where this occurs.

- -

a) $f(x) \equiv -2(x^2 - 5x) + 7$

> Divide the first two terms by -2.

$(x^2 - 5x) \equiv (x - 2.5)^2 - 6.25$
So $f(x) \equiv -2[(x - 2.5)^2 - 6.25] + 7$
      $\equiv 2(x \quad 2.5)^2 + 12.5 + 7$
      $\equiv -2(x - 2.5)^2 + 19.5$

> Complete the square on the expression in brackets.

b) $a = -2 < 0$
so $f(x)$ has a maximum value.
Maximum $= 19.5$
when $-2(x - 2.5)^2 = 0$
             $x = 2.5$

> If $a > 0$ then the function has a minimum value.

▶ $a(x + p)^2 + q$ for $a > 0$ has a minimum $= q$ for $x = -p$
                   for $a < 0$ has a maximum $= q$ for $x = -p$

Exercise 2.2

1 Solve these equations.

    a) $(x + 5)^2 = 9$ **b)** $(x - 3)^2 = 14$

    c) $4(x - 5)^2 - 20 = 0$ **d)** $(2x + 1)^2 - 6 = 11$

2 Put these expressions into the form $(x + p)^2 + q$.

    a) $x^2 + 2x$ **b)** $x^2 - 3x$

    c) $x^2 - 2x + 7$ **d)** $x^2 + 15x - 9$

3 Solve these equations by completing the square.

    a) $x^2 + 6x + 8 = 0$ **b)** $x^2 - 8x - 10 = 0$

    c) $x^2 - 12x = 9$ **d)** $x^2 + 7x + 5 = 0$

p.34 **4** What happens when you try to solve these equations?

    a) $x^2 + 9 = 0$ **b)** $(x - 4)^2 = -25$

    c) $x^2 + 4x + 6 = 0$

5 Put these expressions into the form $a(x + p)^2 + q$.

    a) $2x^2 + 12x + 7$ **b)** $5x^2 - 8x - 4$

    c) $-x^2 + 16x - 9$ **d)** $-6x^2 - 13x + 22$

6 Solve these equations by completing the square.

    a) $2x^2 + 16x + 3 = 0$ **b)** $-x^2 - 6x + 21 = 0$

7 For each of the following expressions

    i) Find the maximum or minimum value of the expression

    ii) Find the value of x which gives this maximum or minimum

    iii) State whether it is a maximum or a minimum.

    a) $(x - 7)^2 + 9$ **b)** $-5(x + 2)^2 - 15$

    c) $x^2 + 4x$ **d)** $-x^2 + 8x$

    e) $x^2 - 18x - 2$ **f)** $4x^2 + 12x + 6$

    g) $-5x^2 - 12x - 3$

8 A quadratic function is in the form $f(x) \equiv x^2 + bx + c$.
   $f(x)$ has a minimum value of 3.
   This minimum occurs when $x = -8$.
   Find the values of the constants b and c.

9 An arch is modelled by the equation $y = 13 - 0.5(x - 5)^2$ for
   $0 \leq x \leq 10$, where x metres is the horizontal distance and y metres is
   the height, measured from a fixed point O at ground level.
   Find **a)** the greatest height of the arch above O
         b) the horizontal distance from O where this height occurs
         c) the height of the arch at its end points.

10 Errol and Ji use the equation $y = 0.5x^2$ to plot a virtual skateboard
   ramp. They want to create another ramp of the same shape, with its
   lowest point at $(-5, 1)$. Find the equation of the second ramp.

11 A goalkeeper takes a goal kick in a football match. The flight of the ball
   can be modelled by the equation $y = 0.01x\,(70 - x)$, where x metres is
   the horizontal distance and y metres is the height, measured from a
   fixed point O at ground level.
   a) Show that y can be written as $y = -0.01(x + p)^2 + q$
   b) Find the greatest height of the ball.
   c) Find the horizontal distance from O where this height occurs.

12 You can attempt to solve any quadratic equation by completing the
   square and if it has any solutions you will find them.

p.34

   So what happens if you start with
   the general quadratic equation $ax^2 + bx + c = 0$?
   Because the RHS $= 0$, you can
   divide through by a. $x^2 + \dfrac{b}{a}x + \dfrac{c}{a} = 0$

   By completing the square,
   show that $\left(x + \dfrac{b}{2a}\right)^2 = \dfrac{b^2 - 4ac}{4a^2}$

   and hence that $x = \dfrac{-b + \sqrt{\left(b^2 - 4ac\right)}}{2a}$

   or $x = \dfrac{-b - \sqrt{\left(b^2 - 4ac\right)}}{2a}$

2.3 The quadratic formula

Question **12**, exercise **2.2** shows you how to solve a general quadratic equation by completing the square.

> ► The **quadratic formula** can be used to solve any quadratic equation that has solutions
>
> If $ax^2 + bx + c = 0$
>
> Then $x = \dfrac{-b \pm \sqrt{(b^2 - 4ac)}}{2a}$

The symbol "$\pm$" means consider both the positive and negative possibilities.

$$x = \frac{-b + \sqrt{(b^2 - 4ac)}}{2a} \quad \text{and} \quad x = \frac{-b - \sqrt{(b^2 - 4ac)}}{2a}$$

Consider each alternative separately.

Example 7

Use the quadratic formula to solve the equation $5x^2 - 9x - 3 = 0$
Give your answers to 2 decimal places.

$a = 5 \quad b = -9 \quad c = -3$
So $b^2 - 4ac = (-9)^2 - 4 \times 5 \times (-3) = 81 + 60 = 141$

$$x = \frac{-(-9) \pm \sqrt{141}}{2 \times 5} \quad \text{so} \quad x = \frac{9 + \sqrt{141}}{10} \quad \text{or} \quad x = \frac{9 - \sqrt{141}}{10}$$

$$x = 2.09 \quad \text{or} \quad x = -0.29 \ (2 \text{ d.p.})$$

► The Greek letter Δ (delta) is used for the **discriminant**: $\Delta = b^2 - 4ac$

Example 8

Use the quadratic formula to solve these equations.
a) $4x^2 - 12x + 9 = 0$ **b)** $x^2 + 3x + 5 = 0$

a) $a = 4, \quad b = -12, \quad c = 9$
$\Delta = b^2 - 4ac = (-12)^2 - 4 \times 4 \times 9 = 144 - 144 = 0$

$$x = \frac{-(-12) \pm \sqrt{0}}{2 \times 4} = \frac{12}{8} = 1\frac{1}{2} \qquad \text{There is only one solution.}$$

b) $a = 1, \quad b = 3, \quad c = 5$
$\Delta = b^2 - 4ac = 3^2 - 4 \times 1 \times 5 = 9 - 20 = -11$
You cannot find the square root of -11; there are no solutions.

▶ The sign of the discriminant tells you how many solutions a quadratic equation has.
- If $\Delta > 0$ there are two different solutions (known as **distinct roots**)
- If $\Delta = 0$ there is one repeated solution (known as **equal roots**)
- If $\Delta < 0$ there are no solutions (known as **no real roots**)

Example 9

State what type of roots the following equations have.

a) $x^2 + 8x + 16 = 0$ **b)** $2x^2 - 9x + 7 = 0$

c) $3x^2 + 4x + 11 = 0$

> Root is another word for the solution of an equation.

- -

a) $a = 1, b = 8, c = 16$ so $\Delta = b^2 - 4ac = 8^2 - 4 \times 1 \times 16 = 64 - 64 = 0$
$\Delta = 0$ equal roots

b) $a = 2, b = -9, c = 7$ $\Delta = (-9)^2 - 4 \times 2 \times 7 = 81 - 56 = 25$
$\Delta > 0$ two distinct roots

c) $a = 3, b = 4, c = 11$ $\Delta = 4^2 - 4 \times 3 \times 11 = 16 - 132 = -126$
$\Delta < 0$ no real roots

Example 10

For the cricket ball at the start of section **2.1**, find the horizontal distances from the starting point when it is 7 m above its starting point.

$y = 7$ so $x - \dfrac{1}{40}x^2 = 7$

$\times 40 \implies 40x - x^2 = 280$

$ 0 = x^2 - 40x + 280$

$a - 1, b - -40, c - 280$

$\Delta = (-40)^2 - 4 \times 1 \times 280 = 480$

$x = \dfrac{40 + \sqrt{480}}{2}$ or $x - \dfrac{40 - \sqrt{480}}{2}$

$x = 31.0$ m   or $x = 9.05$ m

p.26

Example 11

The revenue from the sales of x televisions is modelled by the function $R(x) \equiv 220x - x^2$. The cost of making x televisions is modelled by the function $C(x) \equiv 600 + 75x$. Find the break-even points, that is, the values of x where $R(x) = C(x)$.

$R(x) = C(x)$ $600 + 75x = 220x - x^2$

Rearranging $x^2 - 145x + 600 = 0$

$a = 1, b = -145, c = 600$

so $\Delta = (-145)^2 - 4 \times 1 \times 600 = 18\,625$

$x = \dfrac{145 + \sqrt{18625}}{2}$ or $x = \dfrac{145 - \sqrt{18625}}{2}$

$x = 141$ or $x = 4$

(to the nearest integer)

Exercise 2.3

1 State for each of these equations whether they have distinct roots, no real roots or equal roots.
   a) $x^2 - 5x + 7 = 0$
   b) $3x^2 + 12x + 12 = 0$
   c) $-4x^2 + 7x - 15 = 0$
   d) $3x^2 - 10x + 7 = 0$

2 Use the quadratic formula to solve these equations if possible. If rounding, give your answers to three significant figures.
   a) $x^2 + 6x - 11 = 0$
   b) $3x^2 - 7x + 2 = 0$
   c) $-2x^2 + 5x + 18 = 0$
   d) $25x^2 - 90x + 81 = 0$
   e) $6x^2 - 13x + 9 = 0$
   f) $15 - x^2 - 8x = 0$

3 Rearrange and solve these equations.
   a) $x^2 + 3 = 12x$
   b) $5x(x + 2) = 6$
   c) $3x^2 + 9x + 7 = x^2 - x$
   d) $-(x - 6)^2 = 9 - 5x$
   e) $7x + 11 = \dfrac{3}{x}$
   f) $\dfrac{12 - 5x}{x^2} = 4$

4 Solve these simultaneous equations by substitution.
   a) $y = 2x - 5$
      $y = x^2 + 11x - 19$
   b) $y = x + 4$
      $xy - 3 = 0$

5 Errol and Ji design a skateboard ramp which can be modelled by the equation $y = 0.6x^2 - 2.4x + 2.9$ where x metres is the horizontal distance and y metres is the height, measured from a fixed point O at ground level. Find the horizontal distances from O where the ramp is 1.3 m above ground level.

6 A basketball is thrown towards the basket. Its flight can be modelled by the equation $y = -0.1x^2 + 0.7x + 1.94$, where x metres is the horizontal distance and y metres is the height, measured from a fixed point O at ground level, and $x \geq 0$.
   The hoop is at a height of 10 feet above the ground.

   | 1 inch = 2.54 cm |
   | 1 foot = 12 inches |

   Find the horizontal distance from O where the ball is at the height of the hoop and moving downwards.

7 In economics, the price and quantity of a product can be connected by two equations.

- The *inverse demand function* expresses the demand price £P_D in terms of the quantity q thousands.
- The *inverse supply function* expresses the supply price £P_S in terms of the quantity q thousands.

In this model, *market equilibrium* occurs when $P_S = P_D$

The inverse demand function is $\qquad P_D = 0.5q^2 - 7q + 27 \quad (0 \le q \le 7)$

and the inverse supply function is $\qquad P_S = 1.4q + 5$

Find the quantity of the product that gives market equilibrium and the price of the product for this quantity.

8 An equilibrium equation in chemistry gives the equilibrium constant K_C in terms of an equilibrium concentration x. The equation is

$$K_C = \frac{1-x}{x^2}$$

Find x to three significant figures if $K_C = 14$ and x is positive.

9 Mari hits a tennis ball across the net towards Ines so that its path can be modelled by the equation $y = -0.015x^2 + 0.345x + 0.92$, where x metres is the horizontal distance and y metres is the height, measured from a fixed point O at ground level. Ines hits the ball at a height of 2.3 m. Ines has to hit the ball after it crosses the net, which is 12 m horizontally from O. At what horizontal distance from O does Ines hit the ball?

10 If the roots of the equation $ax^2 + bx + c = 0$ are x_1 and x_2

a) Use the formula to find an expression for $x_1 + x_2$ in terms of a, b and c.

b) Hence show that $\frac{1}{2}(x_1 + x_2) = -\frac{b}{2a}$

> $\frac{1}{2}(x_1 + x_2)$ is the value of x halfway between the roots. By symmetry, this is the x value which gives the maximum or minimum value of $ax^2 + bx + c$

11 Set up a spreadsheet which gives the solutions to the equation $ax^2 + bx + c = 0$ when you input a, b and c.
If you want it to state when there are no real roots, you may have to use a logical function of the type 'IF $\Delta < 0$'

2.4 Curve sketching

If f(x) is a quadratic function, you can find where the graph of $y = f(x)$ crosses the x and y axes.

▶ Let $y = f(x)$ where $f(x) = ax^2 + bx + c$ and $f(x) = 0$ has solutions x_1 and x_2
  • The graph of $y = f(x)$ crosses the y-axis at c
  • The graph of $y = f(x)$ crosses the x-axis at x_1 and x_2

Example 12

Sketch the graph of $y = x^2 - 4x - 12$, showing where it crosses the axes

$c = -12$ so the graph crosses the y-axis at -12.

By factorising:
$$x^2 - 4x - 12 = 0$$
$$(x + 2)(x - 6) = 0$$
$$x = -2 \quad \text{or} \quad x = 6$$

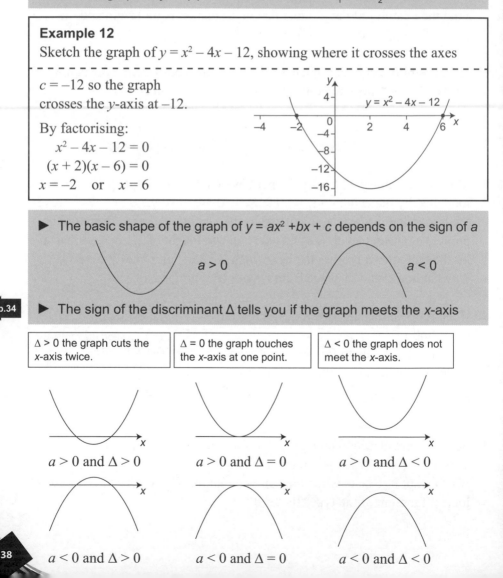

$y = x^2 - 4x - 12$

▶ The basic shape of the graph of $y = ax^2 + bx + c$ depends on the sign of a

$a > 0$ $a < 0$

p.34 ▶ The sign of the discriminant Δ tells you if the graph meets the x-axis

$\Delta > 0$ the graph cuts the x-axis twice.	$\Delta = 0$ the graph touches the x-axis at one point.	$\Delta < 0$ the graph does not meet the x-axis.

$a > 0$ and $\Delta > 0$ $a > 0$ and $\Delta = 0$ $a > 0$ and $\Delta < 0$

$a < 0$ and $\Delta > 0$ $a < 0$ and $\Delta = 0$ $a < 0$ and $\Delta < 0$

A maximum or minimum point on a graph is also known as a **turning point**. You can find the coordinates of the turning point by completing the square.

p.30

Example 13

Sketch the graph of $y = x^2 - 4x - 12$, showing the coordinates of its turning point and the points where it crosses the axes.

Completing the square:
$$x^2 - 4x - 12 \equiv (x - 2)^2 - 4 - 12$$
$$\equiv (x - 2)^2 - 16$$
This is least when $x = 2$
The turning point is $(2, -16)$
This is a minimum as $a > 0$

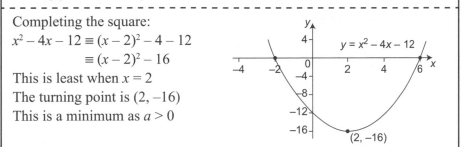

▶ The graph of $y = a(x + p)^2 + q$ has a turning point at $(-p, q)$

▶ The graph of $y = ax^2 + bx + c = a\left(x + \dfrac{b}{2a}\right)^2 - \dfrac{b^2}{4a} + c$ has a turning point on the line of symmetry $x = -\dfrac{b}{2a}$

p.37

In the example above, $x = -\dfrac{b}{2a} = -\dfrac{-4}{2} = 2$ and $y = 2^2 - 4 \times 2 - 12 = -16$

You can also use the symmetry of a quadratic graph to find a turning point.

Example 14

For the cricket ball discussed earlier, find the greatest height of the ball above its starting point, and the horizontal distance from the starting point where this greatest height occurs.

p.26

The equation $y = x - \dfrac{1}{40}x^2$ has solutions $x = 0$ and $x = 40$

By symmetry, the maximum point occurs where $x = 20$.

> If the equation $ax^2 + bx + c = 0$ has roots x_1 and x_2, the graph $y = ax^2 + bx + c$ has a turning point where $x = \dfrac{1}{2}(x_1 + x_2)$; that is, at a value of x halfway between x_1 and x_2.

At this point $y = 20 - \dfrac{1}{40} \times 20^2$
$$= 20 - 10 = 10$$

The greatest height is 10 m, at a horizontal distance of 20 m from the starting point.

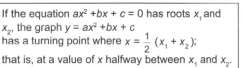

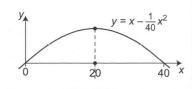

Exercise 2.4

1 For each function below
   i) find the signs of a, the coefficient of x^2, and Δ, the determinant.
   ii) state whether the function has a maximum or a minimum
   iii) sketch the graph, showing **only** the x-axis and the curve (no need to show where the graph meets the axes).
   a) $y = x^2 + 13x + 42.25$ **b)** $y = -3x^2 - 5x - 11$
   c) $y = 21 + 2x - x^2$ **d)** $y = 7x^2 + 3x - 2$

2 For each function below

> Axis intercepts are the points where the graph meets the x- or y-axis.

   i) factorise the function
   ii) complete the square
   iii) sketch the graph, showing the turning point and any axis intercepts.
   a) $y = 2x^2 - 40x$ **b)** $y = 100x - x^2$
   c) $y = x^2 + 8x + 15$ **d)** $y = x^2 - x - 20$

3 For each function below
   i) complete the square
   ii) use your answer to part **i)** or the quadratic formula to solve the equation $y = 0$ (if possible)
   iii) sketch the graph, showing the turning point and any axis intercepts.
   a) $y = x^2 - 20x + 17$ **b)** $y = x^2 + 9x - 6$
   c) $y = x^2 + 4x + 12$ **d)** $y = 4x^2 - 10x - 5$
   e) $y = 0.08x^2 - 0.6x - 1.2$ **f)** $y = -0.62x^2 + 0.41x + 0.09$

4 For each function below
   i) factorise the function
   ii) use the symmetry of the graph to find the turning point
   iii) sketch the graph, showing the turning point and any axis intercepts.
   a) $y = x^2 + 5x$ **b)** $y = 3x - 60x^2$
   c) $y = x^2 - 16x + 55$ **d)** $y = 9 - x^2$
   e) $y = x^2 - 3x - 4$ **f)** $y = 12 + 4x - x^2$

5 For each function in question **4**, complete the square and check that this gives you the same turning point as you obtained in question **4**.

6 For each function below
  i) use the quadratic formula to solve the equation $y = 0$ (if possible)

  ii) use $x = -\dfrac{b}{2a}$ to find the turning point

The turning point of the function $y = ax^2 + bx + c$ occurs when $x = -\dfrac{b}{2a}$, whether or not the equation $ax^2 + bx + c = 0$ has real roots.

  iii) sketch the graph, showing the turning point and any axis intercepts.
  a) $y = 3x^2 - 24x + 9$ **b)** $y = 6x^2 + 9x + 7$
  c) $y = -4x^2 + 12x + 7$ **d)** $y = 0.7x^2 - 5x + 3$

7 Sketch the graphs of the following functions, showing the turning point and any axis intercepts.
  a) $y = 5x - 0.2x^2$ **b)** $y = 6x^2 - 9$
  c) $y = x^2 + 5$ **d)** $y = x^2 + 9x + 18$
  e) $y = 9x^2 - 42x + 49$ **f)** $y = 6x^2 + 3x - 11$
  g) $y = -4x^2 + 5x - 7$ **h)** $y = -0.5x^2 - 2.7x + 4.3$

8 A spout of water from a hosepipe can be modelled by the equation $y = -0.15x^2 + 0.54x + 1.2$, where x metres is the horizontal distance and y metres is the height, measured from a fixed point O at ground level.
  a) What is the starting height of the water spout?
  b) Find the horizontal distance from O where the water spout hits the ground, if $x > 0$.
  c) Sketch the shape of the water spout for $x \geq 0$ and $y \geq 0$, showing the maximum point and the axis intercepts.

9 Errol and Ji design a virtual skateboard ramp which is modelled by the equation $y = 0.4x^2 - 1.76x + 1.92$
  Sketch the ramp for $0 \leq x \leq 5$, showing the minimum point and the axis intercepts.

10 Sketch the graph of the path of the tennis ball in Exercise **2.3** question **9** from the point where $x = 0$ to the point where Ines hits the ball, showing the coordinates of the maximum point and both end points.

2.5 Transformations

Errol designs a skateboard ramp with a parabolic cross-section (side view). He uses the equation $y = x^2$ to model the cross-section.

> x and y metres are measured from a fixed point at ground level.

Now suppose that Errol wants to raise the ramp off the ground by 40 cm. All the x-coordinates will stay the same and all the y-coordinates will increase by 0.4; the new equation will be $y = x^2 + 0.4$

In a similar way, if the ramp is sunk into the ground so that the lowest point is 25 cm below ground level, the equation will be $y = x^2 - 0.25$

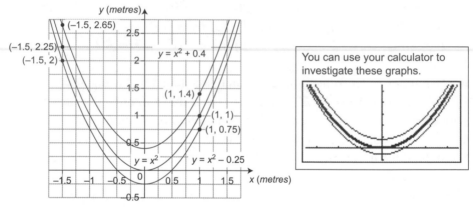

> You can use your calculator to investigate these graphs.

Going back to the original ramp; suppose Errol now wants to have an extra ramp at the same horizontal level but 3 m to the right. Now the x-coordinate is 3 more than it was, but the y-coordinate is the same. So before you square the x value, you have to subtract 3. The new equation is $y = (x - 3)^2$

Similarly, if you move the ramp 2 m to the left the equation becomes $y = (x + 2)^2$

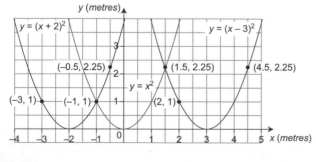

> When you move a graph in the positive y direction you **add** a constant, but when you move a graph in the positive x direction you **subtract** a constant.

If you make the ramp twice as steep, the x-coordinate stays the same and the y-coordinate is doubled. This makes the equation $y = 2x^2$

For a ramp which is half as steep as the original one, the equation is $y = 0.5x^2$

Finally (and this would be difficult in practice and rather pointless) you could turn the ramp upside down and put it in a pit, so the highest point is at ground level. This makes the y-coordinates negative, so the equation is $y = -x^2$

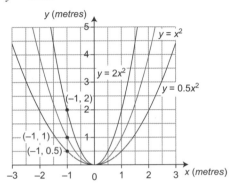

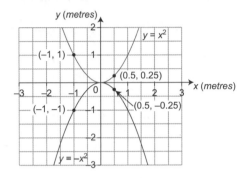

Each of these different transformations of the graph has a particular effect on the equation. You can combine these transformations in any order.

Example 15

Describe fully the transformations that
a) map the graph of $y = x^2$ to the graph of $y = (x - 4)^2 + 5$
b) map the graph of $y = x^2$ to the graph of $y = -3x^2 + 8$

a) The -4 causes a shift of 4 units to the right. The $+5$ causes a shift of 5 units upwards.
b) The minus sign causes a reflection in the x-axis. The 3 causes a stretch of factor 3 in the y direction. The $+8$ causes a shift of 8 units upwards.

Note that this upward shift has to be done last, just as addition is always done after multiplication unless the addition is inside brackets.

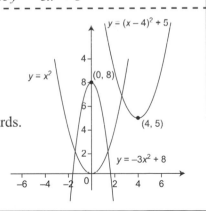

Exercise 2.5

1 Match each equation with a graph.
The graph of $y = x^2$ is shown as a dotted line on each graph.

a) $y = x^2 + 4$ **b)** $y = 4x^2$ **c)** $y = 4 - \dfrac{x^2}{4}$ **d)** $y = x^2 - 4$

e) $y = 4 - x^2$ **f)** $y = (x - 4)^2$ **g)** $y = \dfrac{x^2}{4}$ **h)** $y = (x + 4)^2$

i) $y = \dfrac{(x-4)^2}{4}$ **j)** $y = -(x + 4)^2$ **k)** $y = -(x - 4)^2$

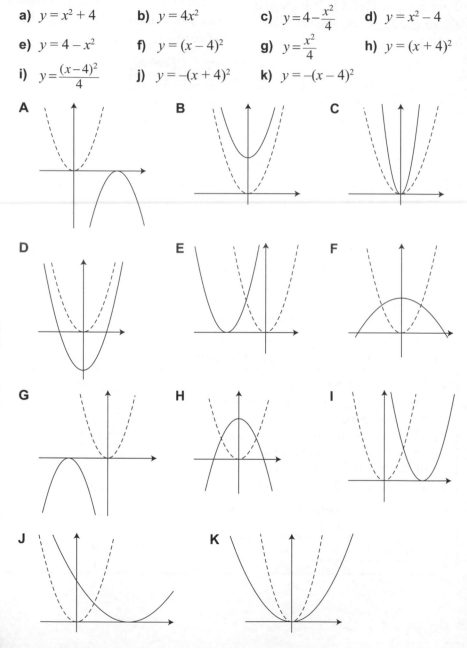

2 Sketch these pairs of functions on the same axes, labelling each graph.

a) $y = x^2$ and $y = x^2 - 5$ **b)** $y = x^2$ and $y = 0.2x^2$

c) $y = x^2$ and $y = (x - 3)^2$ **d)** $y = x^2$ and $y = 3x^2$

e) $y = x^2$ and $y = 3(x + 2)^2$

f) $y = x^2$, $y = -x^2$ and $y = -x^2 - 3$

g) $y = x^2$, $y = (x + 3)^2$ and $y = \frac{1}{4}(x+3)^2$

> Check your graphs on a calculator or computer.

3 Starting in each case from Errol's original ramp, with equation $y = x^2$, write the equation that would follow if Errol

a) makes it $\frac{3}{4}$ of the original steepness

b) makes it $\frac{3}{4}$ of the original steepness then moves it up 0.6 m

c) makes it $\frac{3}{4}$ of the original steepness then moves it to the left 4 m

d) moves it 4 m to the left then moves it up 0.6 m

4 Describe fully the transformation or transformations that

a) maps the graph of $y = x^2$ to the graph of $y = (x - 10)^2$

b) maps the graph of $y = x^2$ to the graph of $y = -4x^2$

c) maps the graph of $y = x^2$ to the graph of $y = x^2 - 1$

d) maps the graph of $y = x^2$ to the graph of $y = -(x + 1.5)^2$

e) maps the graph of $y = x^2$ to the graph of $y = 0.5(x + 2)^2$

f) maps the graph of $y = (x + 5)^2$ to the graph of $y = 6(x + 5)^2$ 1

g) maps the graph of $y = x^2$ to the graph of $y = 3(x - 2)^2 + 9$

5 In Exercise **2.2**, question **9** an arch is modelled by the equation $y = 13 - 0.5(x - 5)^2$ for $0 \le x \le 10$ where x metres is the horizontal distance and y metres is the height, measured from a fixed point O at ground level.
If the arch is moved up 1.5 metres, what will the new equation be?

6 Errol and Ji design a virtual skateboard ramp which is sunk into the ground by 30 cm. The ramp is modelled by the equation $y = 0.4(x - 7)^2 - 0.3$
Ji decides to make all of the following changes to the ramp
- Make it 1.5 times steeper
- Sink it 15 cm deeper
- Move it 2 m to the left.

What will the new equation modelling the ramp be?

Investigation – Quadratic functions

The photograph at the start of this chapter is of Isambard Kingdom Brunel's Clifton suspension bridge.

Total span, centre to centre of piers	702 ft (214 m)
Height of saddles (B and C)	73 ft (22.3 m)
Dip of chains	70 ft (21.3 m)
Height of cable above deck (A)	3 ft (1 m)

It is claimed that the shape of the chains forms a parabola. You can test this claim by seeing how well a quadratic function can be made to model the actual shape. To find a suitable quadratic it is easiest if you chose an origin, O, for the x- and y-coordinates, on the line of symmetry through any maximum or minimum. The equation will then be of the form

$y = kx^2 + c$ for constants k and c.

If O is the centre of the deck of the bridge, immediately below the chain's lowest point, then

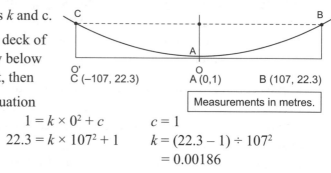

C (–107, 22.3) A (0,1) B (107, 22.3)

Measurements in metres.

Substituting into the equation

A (0,1)	$1 = k \times 0^2 + c$	$c = 1$
and B (107, 22.3)	$22.3 = k \times 107^2 + 1$	$k = (22.3 - 1) \div 107^2$
		$= 0.00186$

So $y = 0.00186x^2 + 1$

To obtain the equation using a different origin, say O′, 107 m to the left of O under the pier, apply a transformation: $y = 0.00186(x - 107)^2 + 1$

ICT opportunity

Use a graph-drawing package to overlay your model functions over photographs of real-life shapes, such as suspension bridges or arches.

Pierre Bézier was a French engineer who was a pioneer in the use of computer-aided design and computer-aided manufacture (CAD/CAM). Whilst working at Renault he developed the use of functions, now called Bézier curves, that can be joined together to model the smooth curves required in the design of cars.

These curves are an example of a spline; originally a thin wooden strip that was bent to define the curved lines found in aeroplanes and boats.

2 Find examples of where splines are used today.

This method works well when there is a turning point and an obvious line of symmetry. In a more typical situation, to fit a quadratic function to three points you must use the general form $y = ax^2 + bx + c$

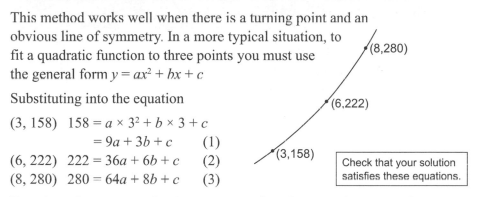

Substituting into the equation

(3, 158) $158 = a \times 3^2 + b \times 3 + c$
    $= 9a + 3b + c$ (1)
(6, 222) $222 = 36a + 6b + c$ (2)
(8, 280) $280 = 64a + 8b + c$ (3)

Check that your solution satisfies these equations.

To reduce these to two simultaneous equations in two unknowns, subtract.

(2) − (1) $27a + 3b = 64$
(3) − (2) $28a + 2b = 58$

3 Solve for a and b, use one of the original equations to find c and confirm that $y = 1.53x^2 + 7.53x + 122$

The use of other functions to fit curves is discussed later in the book.

p.58

p.78

p.96

Project

Investigate using these methods to fit quadratic functions to other shapes or graphs of data found in other subjects. If you vary the three points on the curve does your answer change? How can you decide on a best fit?

Consolidation

You should now be able to
- Factorise quadratic expressions
- Solve quadratic equations by factorising
- Complete the square for quadratic functions
- Find a minimum or maximum value by completing the square
- Use the discriminant Δ to classify the roots of a quadratic equation
- Solve quadratic equations by using the quadratic formula
- Apply and analyse transformations of quadratic functions
- Sketch quadratic functions, showing turning points and axis intercepts
- Fit quadratic functions to data

Use *Receivers* on Data Sheet **2**

1 When the telescope is pointing vertically upwards, a mathematical model
for the cross-section of the bowl is produced. The equation of the cross-
section is

$$y = \frac{x^2}{92} + 50$$

where the x-coordinate is the horizontal distance in metres from the centre
of the bowl, and the y-coordinate is the vertical distance in metres above
the ground.

a) Using an x-axis from -40 to 40 and a y-axis from 0 to 70,
draw the graph of $y = \frac{x^2}{92} + 50$ for $-40 \leq x \leq 40$.   (*4 marks*)

b) Write down the minimum height of the bowl above
the ground in this position.   (*1 mark*)

c) The value $x = 38$ gives a point on the rim of the bowl.
Calculate the height of this point above the ground.   (*1 mark*)

d) Describe fully the transformations that map the graph
of $y = x^2$ onto the graph of $y = \frac{x^2}{92} + 50$ (*2 marks*)

(AQA, 2007)

Use *Wembley stadium* on Data Sheet **2**

2 A mathematical model for the arch is produced. The equation is

$$y = \frac{133x}{24806}(315 - x)$$

where the *x*-coordinate of a point on the arch is the horizontal distance in metres from the left support and the *y*-coordinate is the vertical distance in metres above the ground at this point.

a) Using this model, complete a copy of the table of values below.

x	0	50	100	150	200	250	300	315
y	0	71	115					

(2 marks)

b) On a copy of the grid below, complete the graph of
$$y = \frac{133x}{24806}(315 - x) \quad \text{for } 0 \leq x \leq 315$$
(2 marks)

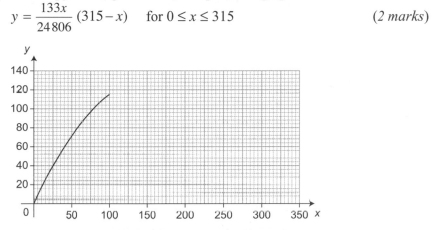

c) Use your graph to find the values of *x* when *y* = 100   *(2 marks)*

d) The centre of the arch is 140 metres above the football pitch.
How far below ground level is the football pitch?   *(1 mark)*

e) The equation $y = \frac{133x}{24806}(315 - x)$ can be rearranged into the form

$y = A - 0.00536(B - x)^2$ where *A* and *B* are constants.
Find the values of *A* and *B*.   *(3 marks)*

f) How are the values of *A* and *B* connected to the dimensions of the arch?   *(2 marks)*

(AQA, 2011)

49

Use *Ticket sales* on Data Sheet **2**

3 A model for the number of tickets sold, N, at time t days after they went on sale is given by the equation

$$N = 20t - t^2 \qquad \text{for} \qquad 0 \leq t \leq 20$$

Use this model to answer the following questions.

a) On a grid with t from 0 to 30 days and N from 0 to 100, plot the graph of N against t for $0 \leq t \leq 20$. *(3 marks)*

b) Write down the maximum number of tickets sold in one day and the value of t at the maximum. *(2 marks)*

c) For how many days were the tickets on sale? *(1 mark)*

d) i) Rearrange $20t - t^2$ in the form $p - (t - q)^2$ where p and q are constants. *(3 marks)*

ii) The values of p and q are related to your answers in part **b)**. What do the values p and q represent? *(2 marks)*

(AQA, 2008)

Use *Income* on Data Sheet **2**

4 The demand, d, for an item is given by the equation $d = 150 - 5x$, where £x is the selling price of the item.

a) Explain why this equation cannot be used for $x > 30$ *(1 mark)*

b) The income, £I, is given by the equation $I = x(150 - 5x)$.

On a grid with Price from £0 to £30 and Income from £0 to £1200, draw the graph of $I = x(150 - 5x)$ for $0 \leq x \leq 30$. *(4 marks)*

c) Use your graph to state

i) the maximum income *(1 mark)*

ii) the value of x that gives the maximum income. *(1 mark)*

d) Rearrange $150x - 5x^2$ in the form $p - 5(x - q)^2$. *(3 marks)*

e) State how the values of p and q are connected to your answers to part **c) i)** and part **c) ii)**. *(2 marks)*

f) When the income is £800, find the values of x to three significant figures.

The solutions of $ax^2 + bx + c = 0$ are given by $x = \dfrac{-b \pm \sqrt{b^2 - 4ac}}{2a}$.

(3 marks)

(AQA, 2010)

Use Big dipper on Data Sheet 2

5 a) Use the big dipper graph to find

   i) the height when the horizontal distance from the start is 16 m. (*1 mark*)

   ii) the horizontal distance when the height is 6.5 m. (*1 mark*)

b) The vertical height of the big dipper, y metres, can be modelled by the equation

$$y = 12 - \frac{1}{125}x^2$$

for $0 \le x \le 25$ where x metres is the horizontal distance from the start.

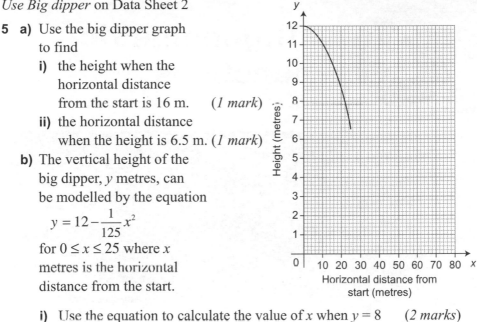

   i) Use the equation to calculate the value of x when $y = 8$ (*2 marks*)

   ii) Why is the model $y = 12 - \frac{1}{125}x^2$ not suitable for large values of x? (*1 mark*)

6 The vertical height of the big dipper, y metres, can be modelled by the

$$y = 2 + \frac{1}{125}(x-50)^2 \quad \text{for} \quad 25 \le x \le 75$$

where x metres is the horizontal distance from the start.

a) Use a copy of the big dipper graph above to plot the graph of

$$y = 2 + \frac{1}{125}(x-50)^2 \quad \text{for} \quad 25 \le x \le 75$$ (*4 marks*)

b) What is the minimum height of the big dipper for $0 \le x \le 75$ (*1 mark*)

c) Why is the model $y = 2 + \frac{1}{125}(x-50)^2$ not suitable for all values of x? (*1 mark*)

3 Trigonometric functions

There are many things in nature and technology that **oscillate** between two extremes, repeating their values in a cycle. For example,

- Musical notes
- Sound or light
- Height of a rotating point
- Hours of sunlight
- Tides
- Alternating current

▶ You can model oscillatory processes using **sine** and **cosine** functions

Sine and cosine are examples of **trigonometric functions.**

> This is often shortened to **trig functions**.

There are other trigonometric functions, such as tangent, but you will be concentrating here on the sine and cosine.

▶ The sine and cosine functions are **periodic**, that is, they take the same values over and over again, repeating after a definite **period**

Here f(x) is a periodic function. The section of the graph between $x = a$ and $x = b$ is the same as that between $x = b$ and $x = c$.

The **period**, T, of f(x) is the distance between two corresponding points on the graph.

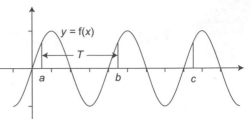

So $T = b - a$ and $T = c - b$

▶ For any periodic function f(x) with period T,
$f(x + T) = f(x)$ for all values of x

Preparation

Before you start this chapter, you should be able to

- **Use your calculator to find values of trigonometric functions**
1 Find   **a)** $\sin 65°$ **b)** $\sin 180°$ **c)** $\cos 82°$ Make sure your calculator is set to degrees.

- **Use your calculator to find values of inverse trig functions**
2 Find   **a)** $\sin^{-1} 0.42$ **b)** $\cos^{-1} 0.85$

- **Use your calculator to find solutions to trig equations**
3 Find a solution to each of these equations. θ is the Greek letter theta.
   a) $\sin \theta = 0.6$ **b)** $\cos \theta = 0.29$

Challenge

Look at *Falmouth tides* on Data Sheet **3**
Zoë wants to model the height of the tide at time t hours after midnight with a function of the form
$$f(x) = a\cos[k(x-b)] + c$$
How does the shape of this function depend on the constants a, k, b and c, and how should you choose values to best model the data?
Can you use the model, or the data, to estimate how fast the height of the tide is changing? What does a graph of this rate of change look like?

3.1 Trigonometric graphs

You may have learnt the following definitions of sine and cosine:

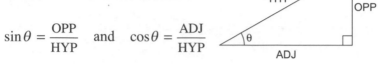

HYP is hypotenuse
OPP is opposite
ADJ is adjacent

$$\sin\theta = \frac{\text{OPP}}{\text{HYP}} \quad \text{and} \quad \cos\theta = \frac{\text{ADJ}}{\text{HYP}}$$

These definitions are valid for values of θ between $0°$ and $90°$.

You can extend these definitions so that the sine and cosine are defined for any angle, including negative angles.

A point P is on the rim of a fixed rotating wheel of unit radius. P has coordinates (x, y) measured from the centre of the wheel.

Unit radius means radius = 1

If θ is the angle that the wheel has turned through then you can define sine and cosine as

$$\cos\theta = x \qquad \sin\theta = y$$

θ is measured **anti-clockwise** from the **positive x-axis**.

You should check that these definitions give the same results as the earlier definitions, when θ is between $0°$ and $90°$.

Starting from the sine and cosine of $0°$, $30°$, $60°$ and $90°$, you can use the symmetry of the circle to work out the sine and cosine of all angles up to $360°$, at $30°$ intervals.

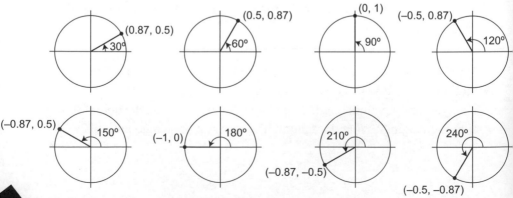

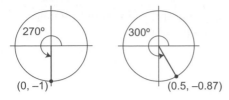

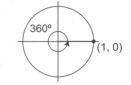

(0, –1)

(0.5, –0.87)

(0.87, –0.5)

(1, 0)

Negative angles are measured **clockwise** from the positive x-axis.

So $\sin(-30°) = \sin 330° = -0.5$

and $\cos(-30°) = \cos 330° = 0.87$ (2 s.f.)

To find the sine and cosine of angles above 360°, just carry on rotating after you reach 360°.

So $\sin 390° = \sin 30° = 0.5$

and $\cos 390° = \cos 30° = 0.87$ (2 s.f.)

Putting all these values in a table

θ	−30°	0°	30°	60°	90°	120°	150°
$\cos \theta$	0.87	1	0.87	0.5	0	−0.5	−0.87
$\sin \theta$	−0.5	0	0.5	0.87	1	0.87	0.5
180°	210°	240°	270°	300°	330°	360°	390°
−1	−0.87	−0.5	0	0.5	0.87	1	0.87
0	−0.5	−0.87	−1	−0.87	−0.5	0	0.5

You can now draw graphs of the sine and cosine functions.

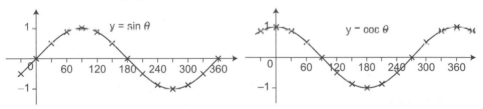

▶ In order to be able to sketch the sine and cosine graphs, remember
  • The two graphs have the same shape.
    If you move the sine graph 90° to the left, you get the cosine graph
  • Both the sine and cosine function have a minimum value of −1 and a maximum value of 1
  • $\sin 0° = 0$ and $\cos 0° = 1$
  • Both the sine and cosine function are periodic, with period $T = 360°$

The graph of the cosine function has the y-axis as a line of symmetry.

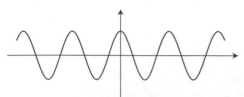

The graph of the sine function has rotational symmetry about the origin.

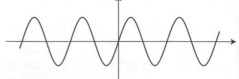

▶ cos(−θ) = cos θ
A function with this property is called an **even function**.

▶ sin(−θ) = − sin θ
A function with this property is called an **odd function**.

Example 1

Solve the equation $\cos \theta = 0.24$ for $0° \le \theta \le 360°$.

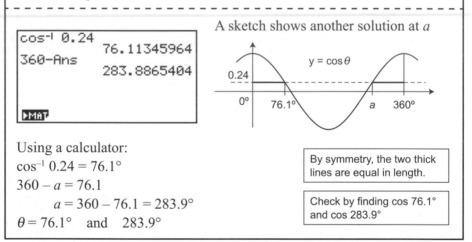

```
cos⁻¹ 0.24
            76.11345964
360−Ans
            283.8865404

▶MAT
```

A sketch shows another solution at a

Using a calculator:
$\cos^{-1} 0.24 = 76.1°$
$360 - a = 76.1$
$\quad a = 360 - 76.1 = 283.9°$
$\theta = 76.1°$ and $283.9°$

By symmetry, the two thick lines are equal in length.

Check by finding cos 76.1° and cos 283.9°

Example 2

Solve the equation $2\sin \theta = -1.06$ for $0° \le \theta \le 360°$.

$2 \sin \theta = -1.06$
$\quad \sin \theta = -0.53$
$\qquad \theta = \sin^{-1}(-0.53)$
$\qquad\quad = -32.0°$

$a = 180° + 32.0° = 212.0°$
$b = 360° - 32.0° = 328.0°$
$\theta = 212.0°$ and $328.0°$

This solution is not in the required range 0° to 360°.
A sketch shows that you want a and b.

Use symmetry

Exercise 3.1

1 Sketch the sine and cosine graphs.

Without using a calculator, state whether each of the following is positive, negative or zero.

a) $\sin 80°$	**b)** $\sin 200°$	**c)** $\sin 400°$	**d)** $\sin 140°$
e) $\sin(-70°)$	**f)** $\sin(-200°)$	**g)** $-\sin 900°$	**h)** $\sin 1400°$
i) $\cos 110°$	**j)** $\cos 270°$	**k)** $\cos(-10°)$	**l)** $\cos 61°$
m) $\cos 820°$	**n)** $\cos 91°$	**o)** $\cos(-1000°)$	**p)** $\cos 340°$

2 State the values of θ between $-1000°$ and $1000°$ for which

a) $\cos \theta = 0$ **b)** $\sin \theta = 0$

c) $\sin \theta = 1$ **d)** $\cos \theta = -1$

3 Solve these trigonometric equations for $0° \leq \theta \leq 360°$.

a) $\cos \theta = 0.67$ **b)** $\sin \theta = 0.89$

c) $\cos \theta = -0.13$ **d)** $\sin \theta = -0.43$

e) $5\cos \theta = 3.2$ **f)** $3\sin \theta + 4 = 1.2$

4 Solve these trigonometric equations for the stated range.

a) $\sin \theta = -0.28$ $(-180° \leq \theta \leq 180°)$

b) $\cos \theta = 0.83$ $(-180° \leq \theta \leq 360°)$

c) $4 \sin \theta = 3$ $(-90° \leq \theta \leq 90°)$

d) $3 \cos \theta - 1.3 = 0.62$ $(-360° \leq \theta \leq 360°)$

5 Create a spreadsheet with the first column containing the numbers from 0 to 360 at intervals of 10, that is, 0, 10, 20, 30,....., 350, 360.
In the second and third columns calculate the cosine and sine of each of these numbers. (You may have to convert the numbers from degrees to radians first – use the radians function in the spreadsheet.)
Now plot the following scatter graphs

a) Column 2 against column 1

b) Column 3 against column 1

c) Column 3 against column 2

Do the graphs look as you expected?

> Radians are another unit for measuring angles.
> 2π radians = 360°
> Radians work better than degrees if you are doing calculus.

3.2 Transforming graphs

Electricity is delivered into peoples' homes in the form of alternating current. In the United Kingdom
- The voltage oscillates rapidly between −230 volts and +230 volts.
- The **frequency** of the oscillations is 50 Hz (hertz), or 50 cycles per second.

This means that there are 50 complete oscillations in 1 second, and one oscillation takes $1 \div 50 = 0.02$ seconds. So the period T is 0.02 seconds.

> ▶ For any periodic function, if T is the period and f is the frequency, $T = \frac{1}{f}$ and $f = \frac{1}{T}$

T and f are reciprocals.

The voltage in this circuit can be modelled by a **sine wave**, that is, a graph of a sine function. What is the equation of this function?

The function $f(\theta) = \sin \theta°$ has a maximum value of 1 and a period of 360°. To model the voltage, you need to transform the basic sine function to a function that has a maximum value of 230 and a period of 0.02 seconds.

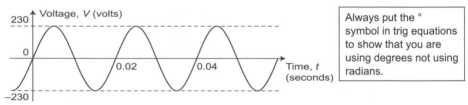

Always put the ° symbol in trig equations to show that you are using degrees not using radians.

The function needs to go through a complete cycle as t goes from 0 to 0.02. For this to happen, each value of t must be multiplied by $\dfrac{360°}{0.02} = 18\,000°$. Look at the graph of $y = \sin(18\,000t)°$.

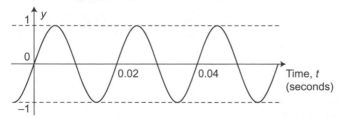

The horizontal axis of this graph is now lined up with the voltage graph. The vertical values are not yet correct.

As you saw in chapter **2**, in order to stretch the graph vertically by a factor of 230, you need to multiply y by 230.

p.42

So the function $V = 230 \sin(18\,000t)°$ models the voltage.

▶ If $y = \sin t°$ is **stretched** horizontally by a **scale factor** of $1/k$ and
stretched vertically by a scale factor of a,
then this gives the graph of $y = a\sin(kt)°$

If the period of the new function is T, then $k = \dfrac{360}{T}$ and $T = \dfrac{360}{k}$

So you can also write the equation
of the transformed function as
$$y = a\sin\left[\left(\frac{360}{T}\right)t\right]°$$

▶ The **amplitude** a of a sine or cosine function is half the difference
between the maximum and minimum values: $a = (\text{max}-\text{min}) \div 2$

Often the graph will have the horizontal axis as a centre line; in this case
a = maximum and $-a$ = minimum

▶ The equation of a sine
function with period T and
amplitude a is

$y - a\sin\left[\left(\dfrac{360}{T}\right)t\right]°$

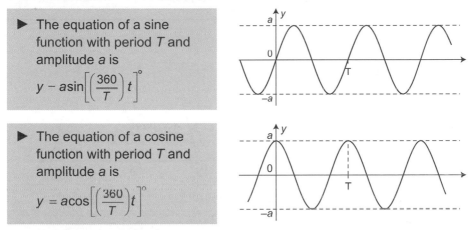

▶ The equation of a cosine
function with period T and
amplitude a is

$y = a\cos\left[\left(\dfrac{360}{T}\right)t\right]°$

So far you have assumed that the sine graph starts at $(0, 0)$ and the cosine
graph at $(0, a)$ and that the graphs have the horizontal axis as a centre line.

▶ The **central value** of a sine or cosine function is half the sum
of the maximum and minimum values: $c = (\text{max}+\text{min}) \div 2$

Sometimes a graph is moved up or down and/or sideways.
You must use **translation vectors** to describe this type of movement.

▶ The vector $\begin{pmatrix} m \\ n \end{pmatrix}$ describes a
translation of m units in the
x-direction and n units in
the y-direction.

If the top number is
– positive the movement is to the right
– negative the movement is to the left
If the bottom number is
– positive the movement is upwards
– negative the movement is downwards

For example, the translation $\begin{pmatrix} 0 \\ -5 \end{pmatrix}$ moves a graph down 5 units.

Example 3

The graph of $y = 5\sin(2t)°$ is transformed by the translation $\begin{pmatrix} 0 \\ 4 \end{pmatrix}$.

a) Write down the equation of the new graph.

b) Sketch the new graph.

- -

a) The translation is 'up 4 units'

$y = 5\sin(2t)° + 4$

For the new graph:

maximum $= 5 + 4 = 9$

minimum $= -5 + 4 = -1$

The period, $360 ÷ 2 = 180$, is unchanged by a translation.

b)

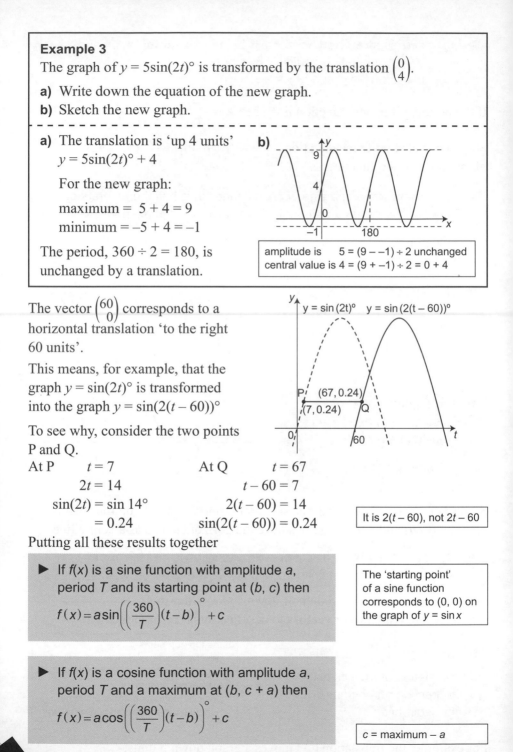

amplitude is $5 = (9 - -1) ÷ 2$ unchanged
central value is $4 = (9 + -1) ÷ 2 = 0 + 4$

The vector $\begin{pmatrix} 60 \\ 0 \end{pmatrix}$ corresponds to a horizontal translation 'to the right 60 units'.

This means, for example, that the graph $y = \sin(2t)°$ is transformed into the graph $y = \sin(2(t - 60))°$

To see why, consider the two points P and Q.

$y = \sin(2t)°$ $y = \sin(2(t - 60))°$

P (67, 0.24)
(7, 0.24) Q

At P $t = 7$ At Q $t = 67$

$\qquad 2t = 14$ $\qquad t - 60 = 7$

$\sin(2t) = \sin 14°$ $2(t - 60) = 14$

$\qquad = 0.24$ $\sin(2(t - 60)) = 0.24$

It is $2(t - 60)$, not $2t - 60$

Putting all these results together

▶ If $f(x)$ is a sine function with amplitude a, period T and its starting point at (b, c) then

$$f(x) = a\sin\left(\left(\frac{360}{T}\right)(t - b)\right)° + c$$

The 'starting point' of a sine function corresponds to $(0, 0)$ on the graph of $y = \sin x$

▶ If $f(x)$ is a cosine function with amplitude a, period T and a maximum at $(b, c + a)$ then

$$f(x) = a\cos\left(\left(\frac{360}{T}\right)(t - b)\right)° + c$$

$c = $ maximum $- a$

Example 4

Zoë (see the **Challenge**) wants to model the height of the tide using $y = a\cos(k(t - b))° + c$ where a, k, b and c are constants.

She uses the following information on maximum and minimum values.

1st high tide = 4.8 m at 3:51 a.m.   1st low tide = 0.7 m
2nd high tide = 4.8 m at 4:12 p.m.

a) Find a, k, b and c and hence write down the equation for y.
b) Hence estimate the height of the tide at 2:00 p.m.
c) Also estimate a time when the height of the tide is 1.8 m

- -

a) $T = 4{:}12 \text{ p.m.} - 3{:}51 \text{ a.m.} = 16\dfrac{12}{60} - 3\dfrac{51}{60} = 12\dfrac{21}{60} = 12.35 \text{ hrs}$

$k = 360 \div T \qquad = 360 \div 12.35 = 29.15$

$a = (\text{max} - \text{min}) \div 2 = (4.8 - 0.7) \div 2 = 2.05$

$c = \text{max} - a \qquad = 4.8 - 2.05 = 2.75$

> The period T of the function is the time between high tides.

$b = \text{value of } t \text{ when } y \text{ is maximum} = 3\dfrac{51}{60} = 3.85$

$y = 2.05\cos[29.15(t - 3.85)]° + 2.75$

b) $t = 2 \text{ p.m.} = 14 \text{ hrs}, \quad y = 2.05\cos[29.15(14 - 3.85)]° + 2.75 = 3.64 \text{ m}$

c) $y = 1.8, \quad 2.05\cos[29.15(t - 3.85)]° + 2.75 = 1.8$

$$\cos[29.15(t - 3.85)]° = \frac{1.8 - 2.75}{2.05} = -0.463$$

$$[29.15(t - 3.85)]° = \cos^{-1}(-0.463) = 117.6°$$

$$t = \frac{117.6}{29.15} + 3.85 = 7.88 \text{ hours}$$

$0.88 \times 60 = 52.8$ mins so the time is 7:53 a.m.

For a function with a straight-line graph, the gradient of the line is the rate of increase or decrease, that is, the **rate of change** of the function. p.6

A function with a curved graph does not increase or decrease at a fixed rate. You find the rate of change at any point on the graph by drawing a tangent to the graph.

▶ A **tangent** is a straight line that touches a graph at a point

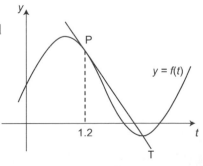

The gradient of the tangent PT is the rate of change of y when $t = 1.2$

> ▶ A negative gradient means that the function is decreasing, a positive
> gradient means that it is increasing

Example 5

a) For the function found in example **4**, draw the graph of y against t and
compare it with the graph on data sheet **3**. Is the model accurate?

b) Draw a tangent to the graph on the data sheet **3** when t = 15:00
   i) Find the gradient of the tangent.
   ii) What are the units of the gradient?
   iii) Interpret **bi**) and **ii**).

- -

a) The model fits the data well
for most of the time that the
tide is coming in (00:00 to
04:00 and 12:00 to 16:00).
However, when the tide is
going out, the model does not
fit so well. The model is ahead
of the actual tide.

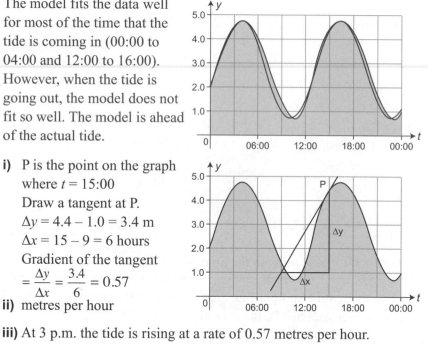

b) i) P is the point on the graph
   where $t = 15{:}00$
   Draw a tangent at P.
   $\Delta y = 4.4 - 1.0 = 3.4$ m
   $\Delta x = 15 - 9 = 6$ hours
   Gradient of the tangent
   $= \dfrac{\Delta y}{\Delta x} = \dfrac{3.4}{6} = 0.57$

ii) metres per hour

iii) At 3 p.m. the tide is rising at a rate of 0.57 metres per hour.

When the height of the tide is decreasing, the gradient of the tangent is negative.	At a maximum or minimum point, the gradient of the tangent is zero.

p.6

Exercise 3.2

> Always check by drawing the graph
> on a graphic calculator or computer.

1 Match the graph to the equation.

a) $y = -5\cos t°$ **b)** $y = \sin t° + 4$ **c)** $y = \cos(t - 40)°$

d) $y = 3\cos(2t)°$ **e)** $y = \sin\left(\frac{1}{4}t\right)°$ **f)** $y = \cos(2t)° + 3$

g) $y = 2 - 3\cos t°$ **h)** $y = \sin(4(t + 20))°$ **i)** $y = \cos(t + 40)°$

j) $y = \sin(40t)°$

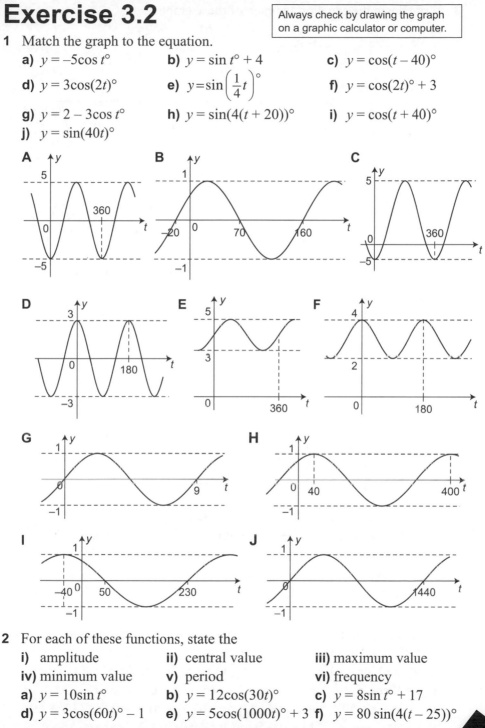

2 For each of these functions, state the

    i) amplitude   **ii)** central value   **iii)** maximum value

    iv) minimum value   **v)** period   **vi)** frequency

    a) $y = 10\sin t°$ **b)** $y = 12\cos(30t)°$ **c)** $y = 8\sin t° + 17$

    d) $y = 3\cos(60t)° - 1$ **e)** $y = 5\cos(1000t)° + 3$ **f)** $y = 80\sin(4(t - 25))°$

3 Write down the equation for each of these graphs.

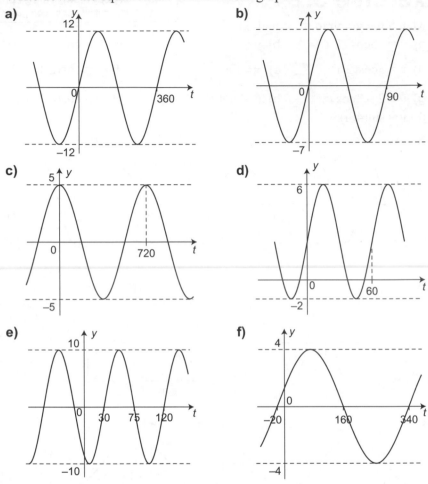

a)

b)

c)

d)

e)

f)

4 Sketch these graphs, showing at least one complete cycle.
State the coordinates of the maximum and minimum points.

a) $y = 8\sin t°$

b) $y = 6\cos t°$

c) $y = \sin(5t)°$

d) $y = \cos(90t)°$

e) $y = \cos t° - 3$

f) $y = 8\sin t° + 5$

g) $y = 12\sin(3t)°$

h) $y = 0.5\cos(10t)° + 2$

i) $y = 3\sin(t - 20)°$

j) $y = 2\cos(4(t + 30))°$

5 For each equation, draw the graph using a calculator or computer.
State the transformations that map the graph of $y = \cos x$,
for **a)** to **c)**, or $y = \sin x$, for **d)** to **h)**, to the graph of the given function.

a) $y = 8\cos x°$

b) $y = \cos x° - 0.5$

c) $y = \sin x$

d) $y = \sin(x + 50)°$

e) $y = \sin(3(x + 50)°)$

f) $y = 0.5\sin(3(x + 50)°)$

g) $y = \cos x$

h) $y = 0.5\sin((3(x + 50)° + 1.2)$

6 For each of the following equations find two positive solutions.

   a) $2\sin(3x)° + 5 = 7$ **b)** $4 - 1.5\cos(0.5x)° = 4$

   c) $\cos(2(30 - x)°) = -0.75$ **d)** $5\sin(2x - 30)° = 2.2$

7 Carry out the following transformations, starting in each case with the graph of $y = \sin x°$. Write down the resulting equation. Sketch the graph.

   a) Vertical stretch, scale factor 4

   b) Vertical stretch, scale factor 4; then translation by $\begin{pmatrix} 0 \\ -2 \end{pmatrix}$

   c) Translation by $\begin{pmatrix} -90 \\ 0 \end{pmatrix}$

> What do you notice about the graph in **7c)**?

8 Carry out the following transformations, starting in each case with the graph of $y = \cos x°$. Write down the resulting equation and sketch the graph.

   a) Horizontal stretch, scale factor $\dfrac{1}{5}$

   b) Horizontal stretch, scale factor $\dfrac{1}{5}$; then vertical stretch, scale factor 2

   c) Horizontal stretch, scale factor $\dfrac{1}{5}$; then vertical stretch, scale factor 2; then translation by $\begin{pmatrix} 0 \\ 3 \end{pmatrix}$

   d) Translation by $\begin{pmatrix} 20 \\ 0 \end{pmatrix}$; then horizontal stretch, scale factor $\frac{1}{4}$; then vertical stretch, scale factor 3; then translation by $\begin{pmatrix} 0 \\ -7 \end{pmatrix}$

9 A flywheel in an engine has a radius of 0.1 metres. It rotates at 3000 rpm (revolutions per minute). A point P on the edge of the flywheel has height y metres above the centre of the wheel at time t seconds.

   y can be modelled by a function of the form $y = a \sin kt$.

   a) Find the constants a and k

   b) Use the model to find the height of P after 0.00128 seconds.

   c) Use the model to find the first time when $y = 0.07$ m.

   d) The speed increases to 4500 rpm. Write down the new equation for y.

10 Use the *Falmouth tides* graph on Data Sheet **3**

   Zoë estimates the rate of change of the height of the tide by drawing tangents to the graph at intervals of 1 hour, and finding their gradients. She then draws a graph of the rate of change of height against time. Draw this graph and suggest a type of function that Zoë could use to model the rate of change of the height of the tide.

Investigation – trigonometric functions

(Jean Baptiste) Joseph Fourier was an orphan who rose to prominence in revolutionary France and was scientific advisor to Napoleon on his expedition to Egypt. He discovered the equation that governs the flow of heat and was the first to appreciate the greenhouse effect in regulating the Earth's temperature.

He also introduced the idea that many periodic functions could be described as a sum of sine and cosine terms, triggering significant developments in mathematics and its applications.

$$f(x) = a_0 + a_1 \sin x + a_2 \sin 2x + \ldots + b_1 \cos x + b_2 \cos 2x + \ldots$$

1 Find examples of where Fourier series are used today.

Fourier series provide a natural way to describe 'periodic' functions. The graph shows the height of the tide at Falmouth, Cornwall for the 13th to 18th April in 2012.

Research

Find out how trigonometric series are used to model periodic functions.

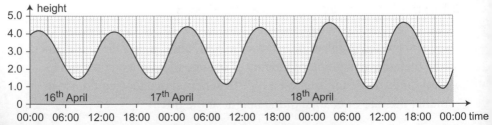

2 List the main features of the graph (period, central value, amplitude) and identify any day-to-day variations.

Tides are caused by the gravitational pull of the Moon and the Sun. The shape of the coastline and sea floor can also have a large local influence.

3 For a body of mass M at a distance R, the gravitational and tidal forces follow inverse square and inverse cube laws respectively. What are the relative sizes of these forces for the sun and the moon?

$$F_G = k_1 \frac{M}{R^2}$$

p.102

and $\quad F_T = k_2 \dfrac{M}{R^3}$

The gravity exerted by a solar body pulls the oceans towards its centre. Since the Earth rotates on its axis, the Moon rotates about the Earth and both rotate about the Sun, the directions of these pulls vary over time. The fact that the Earth rotates results in two tides a day; since the moon also moves this gives a 12.421 hour period.

Quarter moon
Neap tide

New moon Spring tide

4 Explain why the period is 12.421 hours.

Hint: the minute and hour hands of a clock are parallel at 12:00; they are next (anti) parallel at 12:32.7272...

When the Sun, Earth and Moon are aligned, a new moon or a full moon, then the gravitational pulls are aligned and the tides are highest. There are also longer period variations caused by the fact that the Earth and Moon follow elliptical, not circular, orbits so that their distance and hence gravitational influence varies throughout the year.

Project

Find tide tables for a particular location and use them to plot a graph of the tidal height for a period of several days. Can you find a function that will accurately model your data? Start by looking at one part of the graph. Does a trigonometric or a quadratic function

ICT opportunity

Use a graph drawing package to display your data and the function(s) that you use to model it.

work best? How can you decide? How can you describe the whole interval? Can your chosen model be made to work for different locations and for different times of the year?

Consolidation

Check out

You should now be able to
- Sketch sine and cosine graphs
- Solve trigonometric equations
- Find the period and amplitude of a trigonometric function
- Apply transformations, including the use of translation vectors, to trigonometric graphs
- Use trigonometric functions to model real-life situations
- Find the gradient of a graph and state its units
- Interpret the gradient of a graph

Use *Fairground* on Data Sheet **3**

1 A model for the height, h metres, of a seat above the ground at time t seconds after the start of the ride is given by the equation
$$h = 9.7 - 8\cos(20t)°$$

a) Use a copy of the grid opposite to complete the graph of h against t for $0 \leq t \leq 20$.   *(4 marks)*

b) i) What is the maximum height of a seat predicted by the model?   *(1 mark)*

    ii) What is the value of t at the maximum height?   *(1 mark)*

c) i) Find the gradient of the graph when $t = 7$.   *(2 marks)*

    ii) State the units of the gradient.   *(1 mark)*

    iii) What information does the gradient give?   *(1 mark)*

d) For the curve with equation $h = 9.7 - 8\cos(20t)°$, state

    i) the amplitude   *(1 mark)*

    ii) the period.   *(1 mark)*

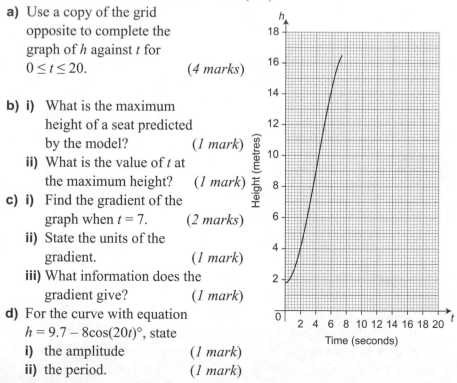

Height (metres)

Time (seconds)

e) The vertical speed, v m/s, of a seat can be modelled by

the equation $v = \dfrac{160\pi}{180}\sin(20t)°$

   i) Find the first two values of t when v is a maximum.   (*2 marks*)

   ii) Find the two values of h when v is zero.   (*3 marks*)

                                                    (AQA 2007)

Use *Temperature* on Data Sheet **3**

2 The average temperature, T° Centigrade, can be modelled by the

equation $T = -12 + 30\sin\left(\dfrac{360}{52}w - 90\right)°$

where w weeks is the number of weeks since the first of January.

a) Draw the graph of $T = -12 + 30\sin\left(\dfrac{360}{52}w - 90\right)°$

for $0 \leq w \leq 52$.   (*4 marks*)

Use a w-axis from 0 to 60 and a T-axis from -45 to 25.

w	0	13	26	39	52
T					

b) For how many weeks in the year is the average temperature
above $0\ °C$?   (*2 marks*)

c) Find w when the temperature is increasing at its fastest rate.

                                                      (*1 mark*)

d) i) Describe fully the transformation that maps the graph
of the function $T = \sin w$ onto the graph of the function
$T = -12 + \sin w$ (*2 marks*)

   ii) Describe fully the transformation that maps the graph of the
function $T = \sin w$ onto the graph of the function
$T = 30\sin w$ (*1 mark*)

                                                    (AQA 2009)

Use *Blyth Tides* on Data Sheet **3**

3 The height of the tide, h metres, can be modelled by the equation
$h = 4.0 + 2.2\sin(30t)°$ for $0 \le t \le 12$
where t hours is the number of hours since midnight.

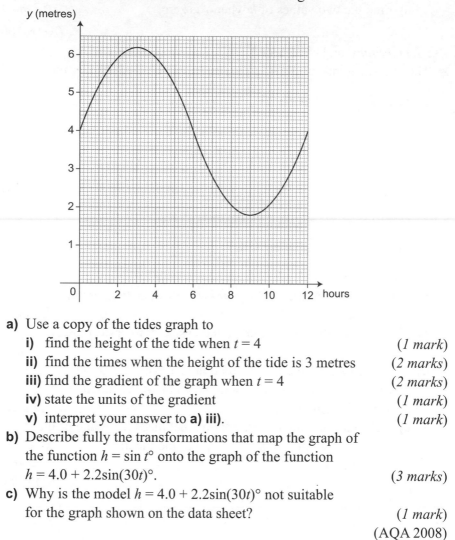

y (metres)

a) Use a copy of the tides graph to
   i) find the height of the tide when $t = 4$ *(1 mark)*
   ii) find the times when the height of the tide is 3 metres   *(2 marks)*
   iii) find the gradient of the graph when $t = 4$ *(2 marks)*
   iv) state the units of the gradient   *(1 mark)*
   v) interpret your answer to **a) iii)**.   *(1 mark)*
b) Describe fully the transformations that map the graph of
the function $h = \sin t°$ onto the graph of the function
$h = 4.0 + 2.2\sin(30t)°$.   *(3 marks)*
c) Why is the model $h = 4.0 + 2.2\sin(30t)°$ not suitable
for the graph shown on the data sheet?   *(1 mark)*

(AQA 2008)

Use *Sunrise* on Data Sheet **3**

4 a) A model for the time of sunset, *t* hours, in terms of the number of weeks, *w*, is given by the equation

$$t = 19 + 2.5\cos\left(\frac{360}{52}(w+13)\right)^{\circ}$$

i) Complete a copy of the table of values.

w	0	13	26	39	52
t					

(2 marks)

ii) On a copy of the sunrise graph below, plot the graph of *t* against *w* for $0 \leq w \leq 52$. *(3 marks)*

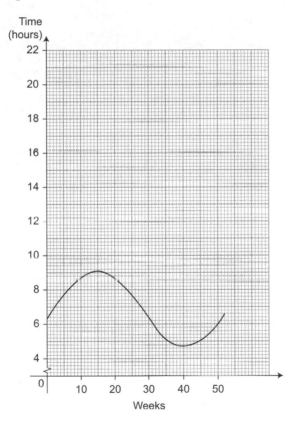

iii) What is the time of the earliest sunset predicted by the model?

(1 mark)

iv) What is the time of the latest sunset predicted by the model?

(1 mark)

(AQA 2009)

4

Indices, power laws and logarithms

In Chapters **1** and **2** linear and quadratic functions were used to model situations where straight lines and parabolic shapes arose. Graphs of powers of x, other than 1 and 2, also have distinctive shapes which can be used to model different situations. These include negative (reciprocal) and fractional powers such as x^{-2} and $x^{\frac{1}{2}}$.

Combining powers of x leads to the laws of indices, whilst finding the power of x which gives a desired number leads to logarithms. Historically logarithms were very important because they allowed the time-consuming processes of multiplication and division to be replaced by the much simpler and faster operations of addition and subtraction.

Today powers and logarithms play important roles in helping to describe the real world. For example, Newtonian gravity uses an inverse square law, whilst the period of a pendulum is determined by the square root of its length. Logarithms provide a natural way of compressing scales which cover several orders of magnitude (1, 10, 100, 1000,…) to more manageable linear scales

(0, 1, 2, 3,…). Human eyes and ears do such conversions automatically. Examples of logarithmic scales are decibels for loudness, pH for acidity, the Richter scale for earthquakes and stellar magnitudes for the brightness of stars.

> Steven's law says that the perceived response to a stimulus such as loudness or brightness behaves as a power of the measured stimulus intensity.

▶ Power laws and logarithmic scales are widely used throughout the sciences and social sciences to model and quantify phenomena

Preparation

Before you start this chapter, you should be able to
- **Use your calculator to find powers and roots**

1 Find   **a)** 134^2 **b)** 7^{11} **c)** 4^{-5} **d)** $12^{0.1}$
        e) $\sqrt{0.035}$ **f)** $\sqrt[3]{90}$ **g)** $\sqrt[4]{200}$ **h)** $(-1)^{101}$

- **Find low powers of small integers and simple square roots and cube roots without a calculator**

2 Find   **a)** 15^2 **b)** 6^3 **c)** 2^7 **d)** 3^5
3 Find   **a)** $\sqrt{100}$ **b)** $\sqrt{144}$ **c)** $\sqrt[3]{64}$ **d)** $\sqrt[3]{27}$

- **Find the reciprocal of a number with or without a calculator**

4 Without using your calculator, find   **a)** $1 \div 8$ **b)** $1 \div \frac{1}{5}$
5 Using your calculator, find   **a)** $1 \div 0.0172$ **b)** $1 \div 324$

- **Rearrange formulae using cross-multiplying**

6 Make y the subject of each formula
   a) $x = \frac{y}{2t}$ **b)** $s = \frac{a}{y}$ **c)** $v = \frac{3a}{4y}$ **d)** $x = \frac{4\pi}{y^2}$

- **Use numbers in standard index form**

7 Express in standard form   **a)** 2 300 000   **b)** 0.00000000045
8 Express in ordinary notation   **a)** 6.89×10^{-5} **b)** 4.1×10^7

Challenge

Look at *Sound engineer* on Data Sheet 4

Hannah is helping to set up a music venue and has been given two jobs. First, she must advise on how far the audience can be from the banks of speakers and still hear the sound at a reasonable level. Second, she must program frequencies into a signal generator to provide musical scales for the various musicians to use when tuning their instruments.

Hannah has asked you to advise her on what to do.

4.1 Laws of indices

An example of a number raised to a power is $2^5 = 2 \times 2 \times 2 \times 2 \times 2 = 32$
2 is the **base** and 5 is the **index**, or exponent.

There are three main laws of indices.

The first law concerns multiplying powers of the same base.

> The plural of index is indices.

$2^5 \times 2^3 = (2 \times 2 \times 2 \times 2 \times 2) \times (2 \times 2 \times 2) = 2^8$
$2^5 \times 2^3 = 2^8$

▶ The **first law of indices** says: to multiply powers of the same base add the indices

$$a^m \times a^n = a^{m+n}$$

The second law concerns dividing powers of the same base.

$27 \div 2^4 = \dfrac{2 \times 2 \times 2 \times \cancel{2} \times \cancel{2} \times \cancel{2} \times \cancel{2}}{\cancel{2} \times \cancel{2} \times \cancel{2} \times \cancel{2}} = 2^3$

$\dfrac{2^7}{2^4} = 2^{7-4}$

> There is **no** rule for adding or subtracting powers of the same base, for example, $2^5 + 2^4$.

▶ The **second law of indices** says: to divide powers of the same base subtract the indices

$$\dfrac{a^m}{a^n} = a^{m-n}$$

The third law concerns raising a power to a power.

$(2^4)^3 = (2 \times 2 \times 2 \times 2) \times (2 \times 2 \times 2 \times 2) \times (2 \times 2 \times 2 \times 2) = 2^{12}$
$(2^4)^3 = 2^{4 \times 3}$

▶ The **third law of indices** says: to raise a power to a power multiply the indices

$$(a^m)^n = a^{m \times n}$$

> If two powers have different bases but they are raised to the same index then there are rules available for multiplication and division.
>
> $a^n \times b^n = (ab)^n \qquad \left(\dfrac{a^n}{b^n}\right) = \left(\dfrac{a}{b}\right)^n$
>
> If two powers have different bases and they are raised to different indices then there are no general rules.

Example 1

Express as a power of 5   **a)** $5^2 \times 5^6$ **b)** $\dfrac{5^{11}}{5^4}$ **c)** $(5^3)^7$ **d)** 25×625

▶ Continued on next page

a) $5^2 \times 5^6 = 5^{2+6} = 5^8$ **b)** $\dfrac{5^{11}}{5^4} = 5^{11-4} = 5^7$

c) $(5^3)^7 = 5^{3 \times 7} = 5^{21}$ **d)** $25 \times 625 = 5^2 \times 5^4 = 5^6$

Example 2

Simplify   **a)** $t^4 \times t^5 \times t$ **b)** $\dfrac{w^4 \times w^3}{w^2}$ **c)** $(2y^5)^4$ **d)** $t^3 \times y^4$

- -

a) $t^4 \times t^5 \times t^1 = t^{4+5+1} = t^{10}$ **b)** $\dfrac{w^4 \times w^3}{w^2} = \dfrac{w^7}{w^2} = w^5$

c) $(2y^5)^4 = (2y^5) \times (2y^5) \times (2y^5) \times (2y^5)$

$\qquad\qquad = 2^4 \times (y^5)^4 = 16y^{20}$

> Or use $(ab)^n = a^n \times b^n$

d) The bases are not the same so the answer is $t^3 y^4$

You can use the laws of indices to extend the definition of a power to include **negative, zero** and **fractional powers**.

Consider $a^m \div a^m = a^{m-m} = a^0$ by the second law

$\qquad\qquad = \dfrac{a^m}{a^m} = 1$ since anything divided by itself equals one

▶ In general
true for every $a \neq 0$ $a^0 = 1$

Consider $a^3 \div a^5 = a^{3-5} = a^{-2}$ by the second law

$\qquad = \dfrac{a^3}{a^5} = \dfrac{a \times a \times a}{a \times a \times a \times a \times a} = \dfrac{1}{a^2}$

▶ In general
true for every m and every $a \neq 0$ $a^{-m} = \dfrac{1}{a^m}$

Consider $a^{\frac{1}{2}} \times a^{\frac{1}{2}} = a^{\frac{1}{2}+\frac{1}{2}} = a^1 = a$ by the first law

But $\sqrt{a} \times \sqrt{a} = a$ by definition of a square root

Therefore it is reasonable to identify $a^{\frac{1}{2}} = \sqrt{a}$, likewise $a^{\frac{1}{3}} = \sqrt[3]{a}$

▶ In general
true for every $m \neq 0$ $a^{\frac{1}{m}} = \sqrt[m]{a}$

> $a^{\frac{1}{2}}$ is the *positive* square root of a, so $25^{\frac{1}{2}} = 5$ (not -5)

Example 3

Evaluate   **a)** 0.5^0 **b)** $(-5)^{-3}$ **c)** $49^{\frac{1}{2}}$ **d)** $16^{\frac{5}{2}}$ **e)** $8^{-\frac{2}{3}}$

| 'Evaluate' means give your answer as a fully worked out number. |

a) $0.5^0 = 1$ **b)** $(-5)^{-3} = \dfrac{1}{(-5)^3} = \dfrac{1}{-125} = -\dfrac{1}{125}$ **c)** $49^{\frac{1}{2}} = \sqrt{49} = 7$

d) $16^{\frac{5}{2}} = \left(16^{\frac{1}{2}}\right)^5 = 4^5 = 1024$ **e)** $8^{\frac{2}{3}} = \left(8^{\frac{1}{3}}\right)^2 = 2^2 = 4$ so $8^{-\frac{2}{3}} = \dfrac{1}{4}$

Example 4

Express as a single power of t.   **a)** $\left(\sqrt{t}\right)^6$ **b)** $\dfrac{1}{t^3}$

c) $\left(t^{\frac{2}{3}}\right)^{-4}$ **d)** $\dfrac{1}{\left(\sqrt[3]{t}\right)^5}$ **e)** $\sqrt[3]{t} \times \dfrac{1}{t^3}$

a) $\left(\sqrt{t}\right)^6 = \left(t^{\frac{1}{2}}\right)^6 = t^{\frac{1}{2} \times 6} = t^3$ **b)** $\dfrac{1}{t^3} = t^{-3}$ **c)** $\left(t^{\frac{2}{3}}\right)^{-4} = t^{\frac{2}{3} \times (-4)} = t^{-\frac{8}{3}}$

d) $\dfrac{1}{\left(\sqrt[3]{t}\right)^5} = \dfrac{1}{\left(t^{\frac{1}{3}}\right)^5} = \dfrac{1}{t^{\frac{1}{3} \times 5}} = \dfrac{1}{t^{\frac{5}{3}}} = t^{-\frac{5}{3}}$ **e)** $\sqrt[3]{t} \times \dfrac{1}{t^3} = t^{\frac{1}{3}} \times t^{-3} = t^{-\frac{8}{3}}$

You can use the laws of indices to solve equations involving powers.

Example 5

Solve these equations.   **a)** $x^4 = 17$ **b)** $x^{\frac{3}{4}} = 35$ **c)** $x^{-4} = 12$

a) $x^4 = 17$ so $x = \sqrt[4]{17} = 2.03$ **b)** $x^{\frac{3}{4}} = 35$ so $x = \left(x^{\frac{3}{4}}\right)^{\frac{4}{3}} = 35^{\frac{4}{3}} = 114$

c) $x^{-4} = 12$ so $x = \left(x^{-4}\right)^{-\frac{1}{4}} = 12^{-\frac{1}{4}} = 0.537$

Example 6

Kepler's third law of planetary motion states that $T = R^{\frac{3}{2}}$ where R is the mean distance of a planet from the Sun in Astronomical units (AU) and T is the time the planet takes to revolve around the Sun in Earth years.
For Saturn, $T = 29.475$; find the mean distance from Saturn to the Sun.

$T = R^{\frac{3}{2}} = 29.475$

$R = \left(R^{\frac{3}{2}}\right)^{\frac{2}{3}} = 29.475^{\frac{2}{3}} = 9.542 \text{ AU}$

| 1 AU is the mean distance between the Earth and the Sun. |

Exercise 4.1

1 Express as a power of 3

   a) $3^2 \times 3^7$ **b)** $\dfrac{3^6}{3}$ **c)** $(3^3)^8$ **d)** 81×243 **e)** $\dfrac{3^4}{3^{10}}$

   f) $\sqrt[6]{3}$ **g)** $\dfrac{1}{\sqrt{3}}$ **h)** $\dfrac{1}{3^{-5}}$ **i)** $27\sqrt{3}$ **j)** 9^5

2 Evaluate without using a calculator

   a) 2^9 **b)** $5^4 - 5^3$ **c)** 7^0 **d)** 6^{-3} **e)** $125^{\frac{1}{3}}$

   f) $256^{\frac{1}{4}}$ **g)** $16^{\frac{3}{4}}$ **h)** $\left(\dfrac{1}{7}\right)^{-2}$ **i)** $9^{-\frac{5}{2}}$ **j)** $\left(\dfrac{1}{8}\right)^{-\frac{1}{3}}$

3 Evaluate using a calculator **a)** 7^{10} **b)** $120^{\frac{1}{5}}$ **c)** $84^{-\frac{2}{3}}$

4 Simplify

   a) $t^2 \times t^9$ **b)** $\dfrac{y^5}{y^4}$ **c)** $(y^3)^5$ **d)** $\dfrac{t^7}{t^9}$ **e)** $\sqrt{(a^4)}$

   f) $(s^4 t^3)^5$ **g)** $\sqrt{(36b^6)}$ **h)** $\dfrac{1}{a^{-4}}$ **i)** $\dfrac{y}{\sqrt[3]{y}}$ **j)** $\left(t^2\sqrt{t}\right)^2$

5 Solve   **a)** $x^3 = -91$ **b)** $x^{\frac{2}{3}} = 25$ **c)** $x^{-5} = 0.012$

6 The planet Jupiter takes 11.86 Earth years to revolve around the Sun. Use Kepler's law (Example **6**) to find its mean distance from the Sun.

7 Hannah is investigating the frequencies of musical notes. Some notes on a piano keyboard are shown here. From lowest to highest, they are
C, C♯ (C sharp) D, D♯, E, F, F♯, G, G♯, A, A♯, B, C'.

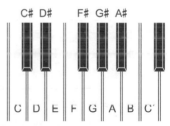

[C' is used here to mean C in the next octave]

The frequency of C is 261.6 Hz. The frequency of C' is 523.2 Hz.
r is the constant ratio of the frequency of each note to the frequency of the note below. So   the frequency of C♯ is 261.6r Hz,
        the frequency of D is 261.6r^2 Hz, etc.

   a) Explain why $261.6r^{12} = 523.2$
   b) Find r, giving your answer to 5 significant figures.
   c) Evaluate the frequency of C♯ to 1 d.p.
   d) Evaluate the frequency of G to 1 d.p.

> You can explain using words, or maths, or both.

4.2 Inverse proportion

Ben, a farmer, hired two combine harvesters last year. It took them 12 days to harvest his fields. This year rain is forecast and Ben is considering hiring more combine harvesters than last year. Ben draws up a table.

Number of harvesters, H	1	2	3	4	6	8	12	24
Number of days, D	24	12	8	6	4	3	2	1

H and D are connected by the equations

$$HD = 24, \quad D = \frac{24}{H} \quad \text{and} \quad H = \frac{24}{D}$$

> When one quantity doubles, the other halves.

This is an example of **inverse proportion**. When H increases, D decreases.

▶ If x and y are inversely proportional, $xy = k$ and $y = \dfrac{k}{x}$ and $x = \dfrac{k}{y}$ where k is a constant

---

Example 7

The equation $PV = k$ can be used to model the relationship between the pressure, P pascals (Pa), and the volume, V litres, of a gas, where k is a constant. When $V = 4.5$ litres, $P = 8000$ Pa. Find P when $V = 3.2$ litres.

- -

$k = PV = 8000 \times 4.5 = 36\,000$

$P = \dfrac{k}{V} = \dfrac{36\,000}{3.2} = 11\,250$ Pa

> The key to solving inverse proportion problems is to find the constant k.

▶ **Inverse square laws** take the form $y = \dfrac{k}{x^2}$ where k is a constant

---

Example 8

Light intensity at a point, I watts/m², at a distance d metres from a light source can be modelled by $I = \dfrac{k}{d^2}$.

At a distance of 2.5 m the light intensity is 60 watts/m².

a) Find I when $d = 7$ m.   **b)** Find d when $I = 85$ watts/m²?

- -

$k = Id^2 = 60 \times 2.5^2 = 375$

a) $I = \dfrac{k}{d^2} = \dfrac{375}{7^2}$

$\quad = 7.65$ watts/m²

b) $d^2 = \dfrac{k}{I} = \dfrac{375}{85} = 4.412$

$d = \sqrt{4.412} = 2.10$ m $\boxed{d \geq 0}$

Exercise 4.2

1   If Ben hired five combine harvesters (see opposite), how many days
    would it take for them to harvest his fields?

2   If $y \propto \dfrac{1}{x}$ (that is, $y = \dfrac{k}{x}$) and $y = 42$ when $x = 5$ find

    a) y when $x = 8$ b) x when $y = 13.5$

3   If $y \propto \dfrac{1}{x^2}$ for $x > 0$ (that is, $y = \dfrac{k}{x^2}$) and $y = 1.2$ when $x = 20$ find

    a) y when $x = 3$ b) x when $y = 30$

4   Ben has 22 cows. He knows that his supply of cattle feed will last them
    14 days. If he buys a further 8 cows, how long will the cattle feed last?

5   The average speed for a particular journey is inversely proportional to
    the time taken for the journey. When the average speed is 45 miles per
    hour (mph) the journey takes 2 hours 40 minutes.
    a) Express the time taken, T hours, in terms of the average speed, v mph.
    b) What does the constant in this formula represent?

6   When a patient has an X-ray, a radiologist 2.5 metres away receives
    a radiation dose of 480 microsievert (μSv). The dose can be modelled
    as being inversely proportional to the square of the distance from the
    patient.
    a) What is the dose if the radiologist is 2 metres away from the patient.
    b) How far is the radiologist from the patient if the dose is 200 μSv.

7   The gas in a container of volume 12 litres is at a pressure of 3800 pascals.
    Using the model in Example 7
    a) Find the pressure if the volume changes to 14 litres.
    b) If the pressure changes to 5200 pascals, find the new volume.

8   Hannah is setting up a sound system for an outdoor music event. She
    measures the sound intensity to be 0.07 watts/m^2 at a distance of 12 metres
    from a bank of speakers.
    She then uses a model in which sound intensity at a point is related to
    distance from the sound source by an inverse square law.
    a) What will the sound intensity be at a distance of 35 metres?
    b) How far from the speakers will the sound intensity be 0.01 watts/m^2?

4.3 Graphs of power laws

When looking for equations to model data, it is helpful to recognise the shapes of graphs. Here are some graphs of powers of x.

p.6

p.38

p.78

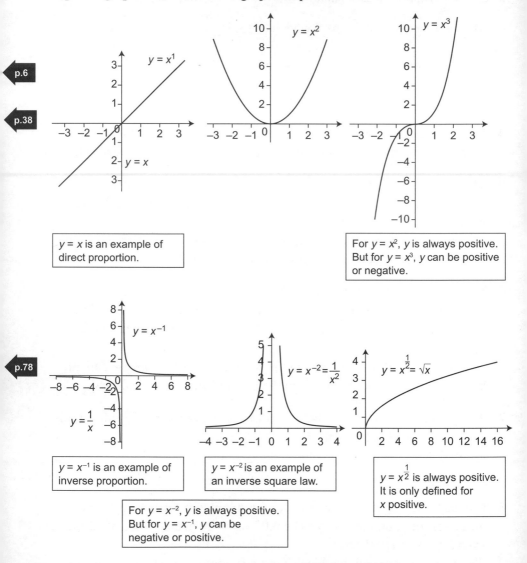

$y = x$ is an example of direct proportion.

For $y = x^2$, y is always positive. But for $y = x^3$, y can be positive or negative.

$y = x^{-1}$ is an example of inverse proportion.

$y = x^{-2}$ is an example of an inverse square law.

$y = x^{\frac{1}{2}}$ is always positive. It is only defined for x positive.

For $y = x^{-2}$, y is always positive. But for $y = x^{-1}$, y can be negative or positive.

Example 8

For the data at the start of section **4.2**, draw the graph of the number of days against the number of harvesters.

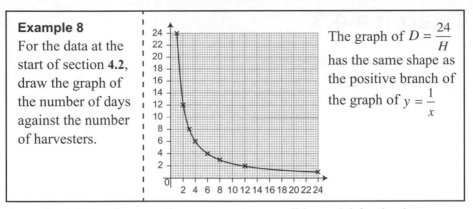

The graph of $D = \dfrac{24}{H}$ has the same shape as the positive branch of the graph of $y = \dfrac{1}{x}$

A graph of data pairs sometimes suggests a possible model for the data. The table shows the diameter, d cm, and the mass, m grams, for some steel balls.

d	0.5	0.8	1.0	1.3	1.5	1.7	2.0
m	0.6	2.4	4.6	9.7	15.0	22.0	32.1

It seems likely that the mass would be proportional to the cube of the diameter, as mass is related to volume. The graph confirms this possibility as it looks like $y = x^3$. So you can try to model the data with a function of the form $m = kd^3$ where k is a constant. To estimate k, rearrange the equation: $k = \dfrac{m}{d^3}$. Substitute a pair of values from the table: say, $d = 2$ and $m = 32.1$, so $k = 32.1 \div 2^3 = 4.0$

The graph on the left shows $m = 4.0d^3$ drawn with the data. Most of the data points are above the graph, so we try slightly larger values of k.

The graph of $m = 4.2d^3$ is shown on the right. This seems to be a good model for the data.

In chapter **5** you will use a different method for fitting a model to data, which involves transforming the data into linear form.

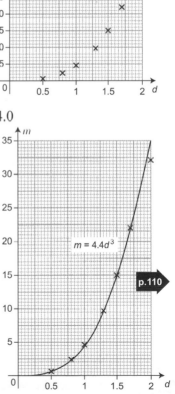

p.110

Exercise 4.3

1 Match the graph to the equation

a) $y = \sqrt{x-2}$ **b)** $y = \sqrt{x} + 2$ **c)** $y = \dfrac{1}{x} - 4$

d) $y = \dfrac{1}{x-4}$ **e)** $y = -\dfrac{12}{x^2}$ **f)** $y = -\dfrac{x^3}{10}$

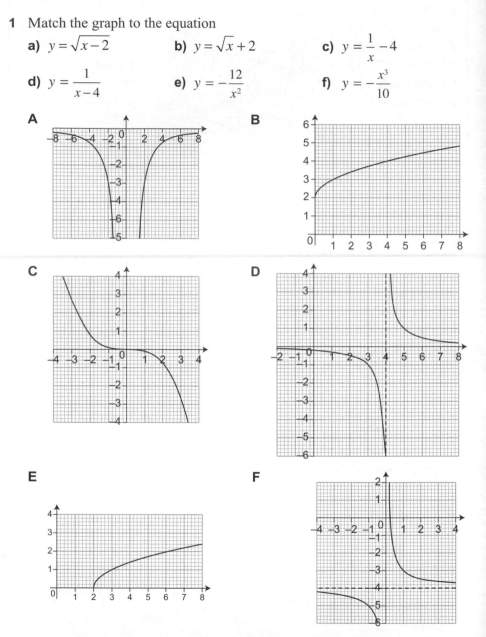

2 The braking distance of a car is the minimum distance needed to stop the car after the brakes are applied. The table shows the typical braking distance y metres for a car travelling at v km/hour in dry conditions.

v, (km/hour)	20	40	60	80	100	120
y, (m)	2.5	10	22	39	58	85

It is believed that a suitable model for these data would be a function of the form $y = kv^2$ where k is a constant.

Plot the data on a graph and find an estimate of the constant k.

3 The acceleration due to the Earth's gravity decreases as an object gets further away from the Earth. The table shows the distance r metres from the centre of the Earth and the acceleration a m/s^2 caused by the Earth's gravity.

r, (m)	1×10^7	1.2×10^7	1.5×10^7	2.0×10^7
a, (m/s^2)	4.0	2.8	1.8	1.0

The data can be modelled by a function of the form $a = \dfrac{k}{r^2}$ where k is a constant.

Plot the data on a graph and find an estimate of the constant k.

4 The table shows how the period of a simple pendulum changes as its length is varied. (A simple pendulum is a weight on the end of a string. The period of a pendulum is the time it takes to swing backwards and forwards once.)

Length, l (metres)	0.1	0.2	0.4	0.6	0.8	1.0
Period, T (seconds)	0.63	0.90	1.25	1.53	1.79	2.01

It is thought that T can be modelled by a function of the form $T = kl^n$, where k is a constant and $n = 1, 2, 3, -1, -2$ or $\dfrac{1}{2}$.

Plot these data on a graph. Compare it with the graphs of power laws in section **4.3**, and choose a suitable value of n.

Fit the graph of a function of the form $T = kl^n$ to the data points, and estimate k.

5 Why do the graphs of $y = x^2$ and $y = x^{-2}$ never go below the x-axis? Can you suggest a rule for which powers of x are never negative? Test it by plotting the graphs of different powers of x on a calculator or computer.

Look back at the definition of even and odd functions. Can you suggest a reason why these names are used?

p.58

4.4 Logarithms

Consider the
following sequence.
$10^{3.5}$ must be a number
between 1000 and 10 000.
Using your calculator gives

$10^1 = 10$
$10^2 = 100$
$10^3 = 1000$
$10^4 = 10\,000$
$10^{3.5} = 3162.27\ldots$

```
10^3                    100
                       1000
10^4
                      10000
10^3.5
                 3162.27766
▶MAT
```

▶ Any positive number can be expressed as a power of 10

Suppose you want to find the power of 10 that gives 5600,
that is, to solve the equation $10^x = 5600$

$$10^{3.5} = 3162.28 \qquad \text{so you know the solution}$$
and $\qquad 10^4 = 10\,000 \qquad$ lies between 3.5 and 4.0

You could solve the equation by trial and improvement

$10^{3.7} = 5011.9$	too low
$10^{3.8} = 6309.6$	too high
$10^{3.75} = 5623.4$	too high
$10^{3.74} = 5495.4$	too low
$10^{3.745} = 5559.04$	too low

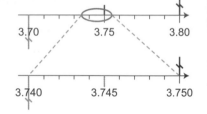

So you know that $x = 3.75$ (to 2 d.p.)

Using the log function on your calculator
gives a much more accurate value.

$$x = \log 5600 = 3.748188 \text{ (6 d.p.)}$$

Check that $10^{3.748188} = 5600$

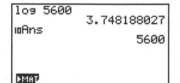

```
log 5600
               3.748188027
10Ans
                       5600
▶MAT
```

▶ The logarithm (log) to base 10 of a number is the power of 10 that
  gives the number
▶ The log to base a of a number y is the power to which you have to
  raise a in order to obtain y

$$\log_a y = x \text{ means } a^x = y \qquad \boxed{\text{A log is an index or power.}}$$

So $\qquad \log_{10} 10 = 1$
$\qquad \log_{10} 100 = 2$
$\qquad \log_{10} 1000 = 3$
$\qquad \log_{10} 100\,00 = 4 \quad$ etc.

The base of a log is written as a subscript.

$\log_{10} 1000 = 3$ and $10^3 = 1000$
These two statements will help you recall
how logs relate to powers.

Example 9

Express in log form a) $10^7 = 10\,000\,000$ b) $10^{-2} = 0.01$
c) $7^3 = 343$ d) $2^{0.5} = \sqrt{2}$

a) $\log_{10} 10000000 = 7$ b) $\log_{10} 0.01 = -2$ c) $\log_7 343 = 3$ d) $\log_2 \left(\sqrt{2}\right) = 0.5$

Example 10

Express in index form
a) $\log_5 1 = 0$ b) $\log_2 1024 = 10$ c) $\log_8 2 = \dfrac{1}{3}$

a) $5^0 = 1$ b) $2^{10} = 1024$ c) $8^{\frac{1}{3}} = 2$

Example 11

Find a) $\log_2 16$ b) $\log_3 \left(\dfrac{1}{9}\right)$ c) $\log_{25} 5$

a) $\log_2 16 = \log_2 (2^4) = 4$ b) $\log_3 \left(\dfrac{1}{9}\right) = \log_3 (3^{-2}) = -2$
c) $\log_{25} 5 = \log_{25} \left(25^{\frac{1}{2}}\right) = \dfrac{1}{2}$

Logarithmic scales can be used to cover a very wide range of values.
For example, the human ear can detect sounds with an intensity as low as
1×10^{-12} watts/m^2 (the 'threshold of hearing'). It can also hear sounds with an
intensity as high as 1 W/m^2 without suffering any damage. The decibel scale
is a way of clearly expressing all the numbers within this range. The sound
level, L decibels, is defined in terms of the sound intensity, I W/m^2, by

$$L = 10 \log_{10} \left(\frac{I}{1 \times 10^{-12}}\right)$$

> Other definitions of a
> decibel are possible.

Example 12
a) Find the sound level in decibels of a sound of intensity 5×10^{-3} W/m^2
b) Find the sound intensity of a sound of 40 dB (decibels)

a) $L = 10 \log_{10} \left(\dfrac{5 \times 10^{-3}}{1 \times 10^{-12}}\right) = 10 \log_{10} (5 \times 10^9) = 97.0$ dB

b) $40 = 10 \log_{10} \left(\dfrac{I}{1 \times 10^{-12}}\right) \Rightarrow \log_{10} \left(\dfrac{I}{1 \times 10^{-12}}\right) = 4 \Rightarrow \left(\dfrac{I}{1 \times 10^{-12}}\right) = 10^4$

$\Rightarrow I = 1 \times 10^{-12} \times 10^4 = 1 \times 10^{-8}$ W/m^2

Exercise 4.4

1 Express in log form
   a) $10^{-4} = 0.0001$
   b) $2^7 = 128$
   c) $16^{\frac{1}{4}} = 2$
   d) $36^{-0.5} = \dfrac{1}{6}$

2 Express in index form
   a) $\log_{10} 10\,000 = 4$
   b) $\log_9 3 = 0.5$
   c) $\log_4 512 = 4.5$
   d) $\log_7 \left(\dfrac{1}{49}\right) = -2$

3 Find without using a calculator
   a) $\log_{10} 1\,000\,000$
   b) $\log_2 32$
   c) $\log_{10} 0.001$
   d) $\log_5 625$
   e) $\log_{13} 1$
   f) $\log_6 6$
   g) $\log_{12} \left(\dfrac{1}{12}\right)$
   h) $\log_2 \left(\dfrac{1}{8}\right)$
   i) $\log_3 \left(\sqrt{3}\right)$

4 From your calculator, $\log_{10} 21 = 1.32$
   So $10^{1.32} = 21$
   Multiply both sides by 10: $10 \times 10^{1.32} = 210$
                                $10^{2.32} = 210$

log 21	1.322219295
10×10Ans	210
log Ans	2.322219295
▶MAT	

   So $\log_{10} 210 = 2.32$, which is one more than $\log_{10} 21$.

   ▶ If you multiply a number by 10, its log to base 10 increases by 1

   Find without using a calculator
   a) $\log_{10} 21\,000$
   b) $\log_{10} 2.1$
   c) $\log_{10} 0.0021$

5 Given $\log_{10} 785 = 2.89$, find without using a calculator:
   a) $\log_{10} 7\,850\,000$
   b) $\log_{10} 7.85$
   c) $\log_{10} 0.0785$

6 How does the log to base 10 of a whole number relate to the number of digits in the number?

7 How does the log to base 10 of a decimal number less than one relate to the number of zeros immediately after the decimal point?

8 Use the fact that $9^{0.5} = 3$ to express 27 as a power of 9.
   Hence find $\log_9 27$.

9 Use the fact that $0.5^{-1} = 2$ to express 8 as a power of 0.5 and hence find $\log_{0.5} 8$.

10 a) Find the sound level in decibels of a sound of intensity 3.2×10^{-6} W/m².
   b) Find the sound intensity of a sound of 84 dB.

11 Hannah is setting up the sound system for an outdoor rock concert. She has to decide if she will need more banks of speakers, or if the ones already in place are generating enough sound.
She wants the sound level to be at least 80 dB at a distance of 30 metres from the speakers. During a sound check, Hannah does not have access to the seats 30 metres away, as the terraces are still being constructed. Instead she takes a reading at a distance of 9 metres, where her meter shows a sound level of 92 dB.
   a) Find the sound intensity in watts/m² at a distance of 9 m from the speakers.
   b) Use an inverse square law model to find the sound intensity at a distance of 30 m from the speakers.
   c) Explain whether Hannah will need to hire more speakers.

p.78

12 In chemistry, the concentration of hydrogen ions (H^+ concentration) in water is given by a pH number. pH is defined as the negative logarithm base 10 of the H^+ concentration.
$$pH = -\log_{10}[H^+]$$
where $[H^+]$ is the H^+ concentration in moles/litre .
A solution with a pH of less than 7 is **acidic**.
A solution with a pH of more than 7 is **alkaline** (basic).
   a) A solution has an H^+ concentration of 0.0000046 M (moles/litre). Find its pH value and state if it is acidic or basic.
   b) A solution has a pH value of 3.5. Find its H^+ concentration.

13 If two stars have (apparent) stellar magnitude m_1 and m_2 respectively,
$$m_1 - m_2 = -2.5 \log_{10}\left(\frac{I_1}{I_2}\right)$$
where I_1 and I_2 are their respective light intensities.
Star A has light intensity 3×10^{-9} W/m² and magnitude 2.4
Star B has magnitude 0.3
Find the light intensity of star B.

4.5 Laws of logarithms

The laws of logarithms are based on the laws of indices.

Note that $\log_{10} 100 = 2,$ $\log_{10} 1000 = 3$ and $\log_{10} 100\,000 = 5$

$100 \times 1000 = 100\,000$ and $2 + 3 = 5$

So $\log_{10}(100 \times 1000) = \log_{10} 100 + \log_{10} 1000$

$5 \qquad = \qquad 2 \quad + \quad 3$

Remember this example.

▶ The **first law of logarithms** says, the log of a product is the sum of the logs

$$\log_a(xy) = \log_a x + \log_a y$$

Rearranging the first example:

$$\frac{100\,000}{1000} = 100 \qquad \text{and} \qquad 5 - 3 = 2$$

So $\log_{10}\left(\dfrac{100\,000}{1000}\right) = \log_{10} 100\,000 - \log_{10} 1000$

$2 \qquad = \qquad 5 \quad - \quad 3$

▶ The **second law of logarithms** says, the log of a quotient is the difference of the logs

$$\log_a\left(\frac{x}{y}\right) = \log_a x - \log_a y$$

What happens when you multiply a log by a number?

A quotient is the result of division.

$$2\log_a x = \log_a x + \log_a x$$
$$= \log_a(x^2) \qquad \text{by the first law of logs}$$

Also, $\quad 3\log_a x = \log_a x + \log_a x + \log_a x$
$$= \log_a(x^3)$$
$$4\log_a x = \log_a(x^4) \qquad \text{etc.}$$

▶ The **third law of logarithms** says, the log of an nth power is n times the log

$$\log_a(x^n) = n\log_a x$$

Two more rules follow from the definition of a logarithm.

▶ For any value of a ($\neq 0$)
- $\log_a(a) = 1$
- $\log_a(1) = 0$

Recall $a^1 = a$ and $a^0 = 1$

The following examples show some techniques that use the laws of logarithms.

Example 13

Write as a single logarithm

> The logs are all to the same base.

a) $\log 5 + \log 3$ **b)** $2\log x - \log y$

---

a) $\log 5 + \log 3 = \log (5 \times 3)$ **b)** $2\log x - \log y = \log (x^2) - \log y$

$\qquad\qquad\quad = \log (15)$ $= \log \left(\dfrac{x^2}{y}\right)$

Example 14

If $\log_{10} 2 = 0.301$ and $\log_{10} 3 = 0.477$, find without a calculator

a) $\log_{10} 6$ **b)** $\log_{10} 5$

---

a) $\log_{10} 6 = \log_{10} (3 \times 2)$ **b)** $\log_{10} 5 = \log_{10} \left(\dfrac{10}{2}\right)$

$\qquad\qquad = \log_{10} 3 + \log_{10} 2$ $= \log_{10} (10) - \log_{10} 2$

$\qquad\qquad = 0.301 + 0.477$ $= 1 - 0.301$

$\qquad\qquad = 0.778$ $= 0.699$

Example 15

If $\log_a x = 5$ and $\log_a y = 8$, find

a) $\log_a (x^2)$ **b)** $\log_a \left(\dfrac{y}{x}\right)$

---

a) $\log_a(x^2) = 2 \log_a x$ **b)** $\log_a \left(\dfrac{y}{x}\right) = \log_a y - \log_a x$

$\qquad\qquad = 2 \times 5$ $= 8 - 5$

$\qquad\qquad = 10$ $= 3$

Example 16

Simplify

a) $\log(x^3) + \log x$ **b)** $\log \left(\dfrac{x}{y}\right) + \log y$

---

a) $\log(x^3) + \log x = 3\log x + \log x$ **b)** $\log \left(\dfrac{x}{y}\right) + \log y = \log \left(\dfrac{x}{y} \times y\right)$

$\qquad\qquad\qquad = 4\log x$ $= \log x$

A power equation can be transformed into a linear equation by taking logs of both sides and applying the laws of logs. You will see in chapter **5** how you can use this method to fit functions to sets of data.

p.1

Example 17

If $y = 25x^3$, find an equation which expresses $\log_{10} y$ in terms of $\log_{10} x$

$$y = 25x^3$$

Taking logs of both sides	$\log_{10} y = \log_{10}(25x^3)$
By the first law of logs	$\log_{10} y = \log_{10} 25 + \log_{10}(x^3)$
By the third law of logs	$\log_{10} y = \log_{10} 25 + 3\log_{10} x$

Example 18

The height h metres of a plant which has been growing for t days can be modelled by a function of the form $h = at^b$, where a and b are constants. Find an equation which expresses $\log_{10} h$ in terms of t, a and b.

$$h = at^b$$

Taking logs of both sides	$\log_{10} h = \log_{10}(at^b)$
By the first law of logs	$\log_{10} h = \log_{10} a + \log_{10}(t^b)$
By the third law of logs	$\log_{10} h = \log_{10} a + b\log_{10} t$

Exercise 4.5

1 Write as a single logarithm
   a) $\log 8 - \log 2$ **b)** $\log 4 + \log 9$ **c)** $4 \log 3$
   d) $\frac{1}{2}\log 25$ **e)** $\frac{1}{2}(\log 4 + \log 9)$ **f)** $\log 3 + \log x + 4 \log y$

2 If $\log_{10} 2 = 0.301$ and $\log_{10} 3 = 0.477$, find without a calculator
   a) $\log_{10} 9$ **b)** $\log_{10} 8$ **c)** $\log_{10} 15$

3 If $\log_a x = 6$ and $\log_a y = 7$, find
   a) $\log_a(x^3)$ **b)** $\log_a(xy)$

   c) $\log_a\left(\frac{1}{y^2}\right)$ **d)** $\log_a\left(\frac{y}{\sqrt{x}}\right)$

4 Simplify, expressing in terms of log x if possible.

a) $\log(2x) - \log x$

b) $\log(x^2) + \log(x^5)$

c) $\log(x^4) - 2\log(x^3)$

d) $2\log\left(\dfrac{1}{x}\right) + \log(x^2)$

5 In each case find the value of the base a.

a) $\log_a 36 = 2$

b) $\log_a 7 = -1$

c) $\log_a 4 = \dfrac{1}{2}$

6 Write each expression in terms of log x, log y and log z.

a) $\log(x^3 y)$

b) $\log\left(\dfrac{xy}{z}\right)$

c) $\log\left(z\sqrt{y}\right)$

d) $3\log(xy) - \log(x^2)$

e) $\log\left(\dfrac{x^2}{\sqrt{z}}\right)$

f) $\log\left(\dfrac{x}{y}\right) + \log\left(\dfrac{y}{x}\right)$

7 In each case find an equation which expresses $\log_{10} y$ in terms of $\log_{10} x$.

a) $y = 5x$

b) $y = x^8$

c) $y = 6x^2$

d) $y = \dfrac{x^5}{3}$

e) $y = \dfrac{18}{x^4}$

f) $y = 3\sqrt{x}$

8 The number of users N of a social networking site t months after its launch can be modelled by a function of the form $N = kt^m$, where k and m are constants.

Find an equation which expresses $\log_{10} N$ in terms of t, k and m.

9 The number of bacteria y in a laboratory culture t hours after the start of an experiment can be modelled by a function of the form $y = ka^t$, where k and a are constants.

p.110

Find an equation which expresses $\log_{10} y$ in terms of t, k and a.

10 Here is a proof of the first law of logarithms.

If $\quad x = a^m \qquad$ then $\qquad \log_a x = m$

and $\quad y = a^n \qquad$ then $\qquad \log_a y = n$

$\qquad xy = a^m a^n = a^{m+n} \qquad$ (by the first law of indices)

$\log_a(xy) = m + n$

$\log_a(xy) = \log_a x + \log_a y$

Prove the second and third laws using similar methods.

Investigation – indices, power laws and logs

Pythagoras (of triangle fame) was one of the first to study the relationship between music and mathematics. He discovered that notes played on strings whose lengths and hence frequencies were in well-defined ratios, such as 2 : 1, 3 : 2, 3 : 4, etc. naturally worked well together.

The 'Pythagorean scale', which was the basis of much European music until the 15th century, is based on two fundamental ratios.

An octave: for example, C to C', ratio 1 : 2

A perfect fifth: for example, C to G, ratio 2 : 3

> Starting numbering at C, G is the fifth note and C' the eighth note.

C	D	E	F	G	A	B	C'
1	$\dfrac{9}{8}$	$\dfrac{81}{64}$	$\dfrac{4}{3}$	$\dfrac{3}{2}$	$\dfrac{27}{16}$	$\dfrac{343}{128}$	2

The table shows the relative frequencies of the Pythagorean **diatonic scale** for the notes CDEFGABC', with the frequency of low C taken as 1 unit.

1 Which notes can you construct using the ratios 2 : 1 and 3 : 2?

2 From C to E is a major third which ideally should be in the ratio 4 : 5, what is the percentage error for the Pythagorean diatonic scale?

> ## ICT opportunity
> Use a MIDI keyboard or a Digital Audio Workstation (DAW) to produce alternative musical scales.

Around the mid-nineteenth century, the system of **equal temperament** (ET) started to take over. In this system, the ratio of frequencies of two adjacent notes is constant, see Exercise. **4.1**, Question **7**. This means the only harmonically 'pure' interval is the octave.

3 What is the percentage error in the frequency ratio for C to G $\left(2^{\frac{7}{12}} \neq \dfrac{3}{2}\right)$?

ET scales have been developed which use different numbers of notes, including 17, 19 and 43. In an ET system with n distinct notes in an octave, the ratio of the frequencies of adjacent notes is $2^{\frac{1}{n}}$.

> ## Research
> Find out about microtonal music and tuning systems.

4 For a given ET tuning, what are the percentage errors of the notes closest to the pure harmonic ratios, 3 : 2, 4 : 3, 5 : 4, 9 : 8, 5 : 3, etc?

Benoît Madelbrot was a Franco-American mathematician who spent most of his career working for IBM. He worked in a number of fields, including the pricing of financial products, but is most famous for popularising fractals.

An early example of a fractal appearing in nature is discussed in his 1967 paper:
How long is the coast of Britain? Statistical self-similarity and fractional dimension

5 Find examples of fractals in nature.

For a cube of side L, the length of its edges, $P = 12L$, its surface area, $A = 6L^2$ and its volume, $V = L^3$. In each case P, A and V scale as an integer power of L. For a fractal the scaling power is non-integer.

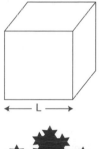

Consider a Koch snowflake: this self-similar shape is formed by starting with an equilateral triangle and repeatedly adding smaller equilateral triangles to the middle of each edge. Suppose the relationship between the shape's perimeter, P, and the edge length, L, of the original triangle is $P = kL^d$, where d is the fractal dimension. Trebling L causes P to quadruple, $4P = k(3L)^d$, so $4 = 3^d$, which upon taking logs gives

$$d = \frac{\log 4}{\log 3} = 1.261859507\ldots$$

6 Find the fractal dimensions of the Cantor set, a Sierpiński gasket, a fractal pyramid and a Menger sponge.

Project

Analyse various different tuning systems, including the standard twelve-note ET system, alternative ET systems and traditional and historical models.
Find the ratios of frequencies of the notes in the scale and calculate how closely they approximate to the pure harmonic ratios.

Consolidation

1 The equation $P = \frac{k}{V}$ can be used to model the relationship between the pressure P pascals and the volume V litres of a gas, where k is a constant.

The table shows some pairs of values of the pressure and volume of a gas in a container which can vary in size.

P (pascals)	1100	2000		3100	
V (litres)	2.5		1.06		0.76

a) Use the first pair of values to estimate the value of the constant k. *(2 marks)*

b) Use this value of k to complete the table. *(3 marks)*

c) Draw a graph of these data. *(3 marks)*

p.76

2 Kepler's third law of planetary motion state that $T = R^{\frac{3}{2}}$ where R is the mean distance of a planet from the sun in Astronomical units (AU) and T is the time the planet takes to revolve around the sun in Earth years. The table shows these values for the planets of the solar system.

Planet	R	T
Mercury	0.39	
Venus	0.723	
Earth	1	1
Mars	1.524	
Jupiter		11.862
Saturn	9.54	29.475
Uranus		84.07
Neptune		164.81

a) Use the equation to complete the table *(3 marks)*

b) Draw a graph of these data. *(3 marks)*

3 Hannah is investigating the frequencies of musical notes. (See Exercise **4.1**, question **7**). The frequency f Hz of a note can be calculated using the equation

$$f = 261.6r^n$$

where $r^{12} = 2$, and the note is n semitones higher than the note C shown at the left of the keyboard. A note has a frequency of 466.1 Hz.

a) Substitute suitable numbers into the equation $f = 261.6r^n$ to give an equation in n. *(2 marks)*

b) Take logs of both sides of this equation and use the laws of logarithms to find n. *(3 marks)*

c) Use the keyboard diagram to state the name of the note. *(1 mark)*

4 Hannah is setting up a sound system for an outdoor music event. She measures the sound intensity to be 0.08 watts/m² at a distance of 10 metres from a bank of speakers.

She then uses a model by which the sound intensity I watts/m² at a point is related to distance x metres from the sound source by an inverse square law to calculate the sound intensity at various distances.

She puts these values in a table.

a) Write an equation expressing I in terms of x. *(2 marks)*

b) Use your equation to complete row two in a copy of the table.

x	10	20	30	40	50
I	0.08				
L					

(2 marks)

Hannah also wants her table to show the sound level in decibels, L. She uses the equation

$$L = 10 \log_{10} \left(\frac{I}{1 \times 10^{-12}} \right) \text{ where } I \text{ W/m}^2 \text{ is the sound intensity.}$$

c) Complete row three of the table. *(2 marks)*

d) Use the first and third rows of this table to draw the graph of L against x. *(2 marks)*

e) Hannah wants the sound level for all the audience members to be at least 90 dB. Use the equations above to find the maximum distance from the sound source that an audience member could be if this condition is to be met. *(4 marks)*

5

Exponential functions and non-linear laws

When you invest money in a savings account you get (compound) interest that is proportional to how much money is in the account. Likewise, the growth in a population is proportional to the current size of the (breeding) population. The rate at which an object cools is proportional to its temperature difference above that of its surroundings. The amount of radioactivity in a sample is proportional to the number of radioactive atoms remaining. In all these processes the rate at which they change is proportional to their current value: they are known as exponential processes and are very common.

► Exponential functions are used to model processes in which the growth or decay of a quantity is proportional to the current value of the quantity

The inverse of the exponential function is called the logarithm function. The logarithm of the exponential of x gives you back x as does the exponential of the logarithm of x. They are analogues of the square and square root functions and reverse each others' effects.

Using logarithms allows you to convert power laws and exponential laws into straight-line graphs. This means that you can use the line of best fit techniques of chapter **1**, developed for linear models, to estimate the constants in a non-linear model.

▶ Transforming non-linear functions to linear form allows you to estimate the constants in modelling equations more easily

Preparation

Before you start this chapter, you should be able to
- **Use the calculator functions e^x and $\ln x$**
1 Find **a)** e^1 **b)** e^{-3} **c)** $e^{12.3}$ **d)** $e^{0.0047}$
2 Find **a)** $\ln 4$ **b)** $\ln 1$ **c)** $\ln 0.1$ **d)** $\ln e$
- **Reflect a shape in the *x*-axis, the *y*-axis or the line *y* = *x***
3 Draw the graph of $y = \sqrt{x}$ for $0 \le x \le 4$.
   a) Reflect the graph in the *x*-axis.
   b) Reflect the graph in the *y*-axis.
   c) Reflect the graph in the line $y = x$

Challenge

Look at *Laboratory technician* on Data Sheet **5**
Anton is looking for suitable models for the following processes.

- Cooling
- Radioactive decay
- Growth of biological cultures

He notices that in each of these processes there is a quantity – excess temperature over surroundings, amount of isotope present and mass of bacteria respectively – that either doubles or halves in a fixed period of time.

Anton wants to find equations to model these processes and to estimate any constants that appear in the equations.

How would you solve Anton's problem?

5.1 Exponential functions

Maria invests £1000 in a savings account that pays 6% interest per annum (p.a.). The table shows how 6% interest is added each year.

Year	Amount at start of year	Interest	Amount at end of year
1	1000	0.06 × 1000 = 60.00	1000.00 + 60.00 = 1060.00
2	1060	0.06 × 1060 = 63.60	1060.00 + 63.60 = 1123.60
3	1123.60	0.06 × 1123.60 = 67.42	1123.60 + 67.42 = 1191.02

A quicker way to find the amount in the account is to use a **multiplier**.

In Maria's case the multiplier is $\dfrac{100+6}{100} = 1.06$

(Amount at start of year) × 1.06 = (Amount at end of year)

Year 1: $1000.00 \times 1.06 = 1060$

Year 2: $1060.00 \times 1.06 = 1123.60$ or $1000 \times 1.06^2 = 1123.60$

Year 3: $1123.60 \times 1.06 = 1191.02$ or $1000 \times 1.06^3 = 1191.02$

Amount of money in the account after t years $= 1000 \times 1.06^t$

For example, after 9.3 years there is

$1000 \times 1.06^{9.3} = £1719.27$

> Interest can be added daily, so t does not have to be an integer.

> ▶ If the initial value of a quantity is A, and it then increases by $r\%$ each year, its value after t years is $A\left(\dfrac{100+r}{100}\right)^t$

> You can also use other time periods.

In an **exponential process**, a quantity increases or decreases by a fixed ratio in a fixed time.

> ▶ An **exponential function** is a function of the form $y = ka^{mx}$ where k, a and m are constants and $a > 0$ is called the **base**

You can use the laws of logarithms to solve exponential equations.

Example 1	
How long does it take until Maria has £1500 in her account?	$1500 = 1000 \times 1.06^t$
	$1.06^t = 1.5$
Taking logs	$\log_{10}(1.06^t) = \log_{10} 1.5$
By the third law of logs	$t \log_{10} 1.06 = \log_{10} 1.5$
	$t = \dfrac{\log_{10} 1.5}{\log_{10} 1.06} = 6.96$ years

Example 2

At the start of one of Anton's experiments there is 0.028 grams of a radioactive isotope. The amount reduces by 7% a day.

a) Find out the time it takes for the amount to reduce by half.

b) How much of the isotope is left when the experiment has been going on for twice the half-life?

As the amount is *decreasing* by 7% a day, the multiplier is $\dfrac{100-7}{100} = 0.93$

If there are y grams after t days $\qquad y = 0.028 \times 0.93^t$

a)
$$0.014 = 0.028 \times 0.93^t$$
$$0.93^t = 0.5$$

Taking logs $\qquad\qquad\qquad \log_{10}(0.93^t) = \log_{10} 0.5$

By the third law of logs $\qquad t \log_{10} 0.93 = \log_{10} 0.5$

$$t = \frac{\log_{10} 0.5}{\log_{10} 0.93} = 9.55 \text{ days}$$

> Here t is the half-life, that is, the time it takes for half the isotope to decay.

b) When $t = 2 \times 9.55 = 19.1$, $\quad y = 0.028(0.93^{19.1}) = 0.007\text{g}$

There is one number that is used more than any other as the base of exponential functions, the number e. Imagine you increase an amount of money by one millionth and you repeat this a million times.

It has then increased by a factor of $\left(1 + \dfrac{1}{1000\,000}\right)^{1\,000\,000} = 2.718280469\ldots$

As you increase n in the expression $\left(1 + \dfrac{1}{n}\right)^n$, you get closer and closer to e.

▶ e = 2.718281828...

> e is used as the base of exponential functions because it makes calculus easier.
> Logs to base e are also used in the calculus.

e is also commonly used as the base of logarithms. Logarithms to base e are called **natural logarithms**.

▶ $\log_e x$ is usually written as $\ln x$
$\quad y = e^x \iff x = \ln y$

e^x and $\ln x$ can both be found on your calculator. In general,

```
ln 2
          0.6931471806
e^Ans
                     2
ln (e^5)
                     5
▶MAT
```

▶ $e^{\ln a} = a$ and $\ln(e^a) = a$

e^x and $\ln x$ are inverse functions; that is, they reverse each other.

Example 3

Solve the equation $5e^x = 34$

$$5e^x = 34$$

$$e^x = \frac{34}{5} = 6.8$$

Take logs to base e
of both sides.

$$\ln(e^x) = \ln 6.8$$

$$x = \ln 6.8 = 1.92$$

Check by
substituting back.

Example 4

Solve the equation $\ln(x + 2) = 0.38$

$$\ln(x + 2) = 0.38$$

Raise e to the power of
each side

$$x + 2 = e^{0.38} = 1.462$$

$$x = 1.462 - 2 = -0.538$$

Example 5

The temperature y °C of a cup of tea which has been left in a room to cool for t minutes can be modelled by the equation $y = 16 + 64e^{-0.065t}$

The negative
power shows y
is decreasing.

a) Find the temperature after

 i) 0 minutes **ii)** 10 minutes **iii)** 20 minutes

b) How long does it take for the temperature to fall to 37 °C?

a) i) $y = 16 + 64e^0 \quad = 16 + 64 \quad = 80$ °C

 ii) $y = 16 + 64e^{-0.065 \times 10} = 16 + 64e^{-0.65} = 49.4$ °C

 iii) $y = 16 + 64e^{-0.065 \times 20} = 16 + 64e^{-1.3} = 33.4$ °C

b)

$$16 + 64e^{-0.065t} = 37$$

$$64e^{-0.065t} = 21$$

$$e^{-0.065t} = \frac{21}{64} = 0.328$$

Take logs to base e
of both sides

$$-0.065t = \ln 0.328$$

$$= -1.114$$

$$t = \frac{-1.114}{-0.065}$$

$$t = 17.1 \text{ minutes}$$

```
(37-16)÷64
                0.328125
ln Ans
             -1.114360646
Ans÷-0.065
              17.14400993
MAT
```

Exercise 5.1

1 Solve the equations
   a) $5^x = 673$ **b)** $2400(1.05^t) = 2900$ **c)** $0.99^t = 0.71$

2 Solve the equations
   a) $e^x = 4500$ **b)** $e^{-0.0056t} = 0.67$ **c)** $300e^{0.07x} = 529$

3 Solve the equations
   a) $\ln x = -0.082$ **b)** $\ln(5x) = 2.476$ **c)** $3\ln(2x + 4) = 15$

4 The amount of money £y in a savings account after t years is given by the
   function $y = 13\,000(1.025^t)$
   a) How much money is initially in the account?
   b) At what percentage rate is interest added to the account?
   c) How much money is in the account after 7 years?
   d) How long does it take for the amount to reach £14 000?

5 Anton (see Challenge) notes that at 12:00 hours, the number of bacteria
   in a laboratory culture is 2000. The number of bacteria then increases by
   18% every hour.
   a) Find an equation for y, the number of bacteria after t hours
   b) Find the number of bacteria at 16:30
   c) How long does it take for the number of bacteria to triple?

6 Anton believes that the amount y grams of a radioactive isotope present t
   days after the start of an experiment can be modelled by the function
   $y = 0.06e^{-0.0078t}$
   a) Find the amount of the isotope present after 30 days
   b) Find the half-life of the isotope (see Example 2)
   c) Use the third law of indices to express y in the form $y = 0.06a^t$
   where a is a constant, given correct to 3 significant figures.

5.2 Inverse functions

These tables can be used to draw the graphs
of $y = 2^x$ and $y = \log_2 x$ on the same axes.

x	−2	−1	0	1	2	3
$y = 2^x$	$\frac{1}{4}$	$\frac{1}{2}$	1	2	4	8

x		$\frac{1}{4}$	$\frac{1}{2}$	1	2	4	8
$y = \log_2 x$	−2	−1	0	1	2	3

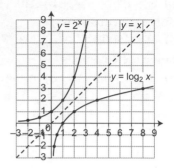

If you compare the data pairs for the two
functions, you can see that x and y swap places.

$y = 2^x$ and $y = \log_2 x$ are **inverse functions**.
One graph is a reflection of the other graph in the line $y = x$.

> ▶ The inverse function of $f(x)$ is written $f^{-1}(x)$
> ▶ The graph of $y = f^{-1}(x)$ is the reflection of $y = f(x)$ in the line $y = x$

Here are two more pairs of inverse functions and their graphs.

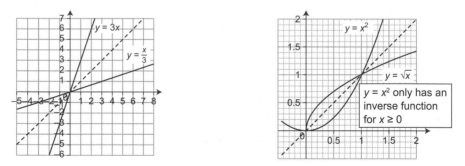

$y = x^2$ only has an
inverse function
for $x \geq 0$

If you find f of a number, then f^{-1} of the result will take you back to the
original number. For example:
If $f(x) = \sin x°$ (and $0 \leq x \leq 90$), then $f^{-1}(x) = \sin^{-1} x$

- On your calculator, find $\sin 70°$
- Then find $\sin^{-1}$ (Ans)
- You will get back to 70

```
sin 70
          0.9396926208
sin⁻¹ Ans
                    70


▶MAT
```

> ▶ $f(f^{-1}(x)) = x$ and $f^{-1}(f(x)) = x$

Sometimes it is obvious what the inverse function is, but not always.
There is a procedure for finding an inverse function.

Example 6

Find the inverse function of $f(x) = 4x^2$ $(x \geq 0)$

Write $x = f(y)$ $\qquad\qquad$ $x = 4y^2$ $\quad (y \geq 0)$

Make y the subject $\qquad\qquad$ $y^2 = \dfrac{x}{4}$

$$y = \sqrt{\frac{x}{4}} = \frac{\sqrt{x}}{\sqrt{4}} = \frac{\sqrt{x}}{2} \quad \text{(as } y \geq 0)$$

Replace y by $f^{-1}(x)$ $\qquad\qquad$ $f^{-1}(x) = \dfrac{\sqrt{x}}{2} \quad$ for $x \geq 0$

Example 7

Find the inverse function of $f(x) - 0.5e^{3x}$

Write $x = f(y)$ (> 0) $\qquad\qquad$ $x = 0.5e^{3y}$

Make y the subject $\qquad\qquad$ $2x = e^{3y}$

Taking logs to base e $\qquad\qquad$ $\ln(2x) = 3y$

$$y = \frac{\ln(2x)}{3}$$

Replace y by $f^{-1}(x)$ $\qquad\qquad$ $f^{-1}(x) = \dfrac{\ln(2x)}{3} \quad$ for $x > 0$

> Check by finding f(4)
> Then find $f^{-1}(f(4))$,
> it should be 4.

Exercise 5.2

1 Find the inverse function of each of the following functions.

a) $f(x) = e^{2x}$ $\qquad\qquad$ b) $f(x) = \dfrac{x^2}{3}$ $\qquad (x > 0)$

c) $f(x) = 4 - x$ $\qquad\qquad$ d) $f(x) = \ln(x - 3)$ $\;(x > 3)$

e) $f(x) = x^3$ $\qquad\qquad\qquad$ f) $f(x) = 4\ln x$ $\qquad (x > 0)$

g) $f(x) = \sqrt{x-1}$ $\;(x \geq 1)$ $\qquad$ h) $f(x) = \sin(3x)°$ $\;(0 \leq x \leq 30)$

2 For each part of **Q1**, use a computer or your calculator to draw the graphs of f(x) and $f^{-1}(x)$ on the same axes.

> Exercise **5.3** has more questions on the
> graphs of inverse functions.

5.3 Exponential and log graphs

▶ All **exponential graphs** have the same basic shape as $y = 2^x$

Consider the graph of $y = 2^{-x}$

x	−2	−1	0	1	2
$y = 2^{-x}$	4	2	1	$\frac{1}{2}$	$\frac{1}{4}$

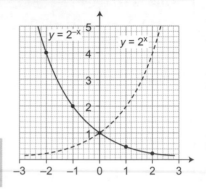

The graph of $y = 2^{-x}$ is the reflection in the
y-axis of the graph of $y = 2^x$. In general

▶ The graph of $y = f(-x)$ is the reflection
in the y-axis of the graph of $y = f(x)$

Here are some exponential graphs, with $y = e^x$ shown as a dotted line.

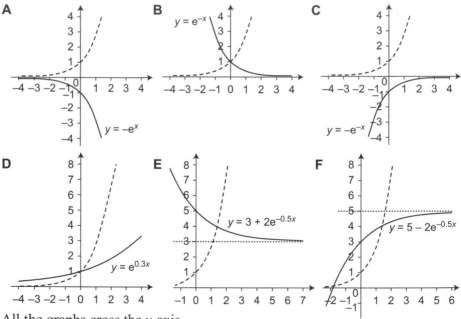

A

B $y = e^{-x}$

C $y = -e^{-x}$

$y = -e^x$

D $y = e^{0.3x}$

E $y = 3 + 2e^{-0.5x}$

F $y = 5 - 2e^{-0.5x}$

All the graphs cross the y-axis.
Substitute $x = 0$ into each equation to find the y-intercept.
For example, in graph E, $y(0) = 3 + 2e^{-0.5 \times 0} = 3 + 2 = 5$
Only graph F crosses the x-axis.

Example 8

Find the value of x where graph F crosses the x-axis.

$y = 0$ $\qquad\qquad$ $5 - 2e^{-0.5x} = 0$

$\qquad\qquad\qquad\qquad$ $2e^{-0.5x} = 5$

$\qquad\qquad\qquad\qquad$ $e^{-0.5x} = 2.5$

Taking logs to base e $\qquad$ $-0.5x = \ln 2.5$

$\qquad\qquad\qquad\qquad$ $x = -2\ln 2.5 = -1.83$

Look at what happens to each graph as x gets larger and larger.

In graph A, $\qquad\qquad$ y becomes large and negative.

In graphs B and C, $\qquad$ y gets closer and closer to zero.

In graph D, $\qquad\qquad$ y becomes large and positive.

> You can say y tends to zero. This is written $y \to 0$

In graph E, $\qquad\qquad$ y tends to 3

In graph F, $\qquad\qquad$ y tends to 5.

Instead of saying 'as x gets larger and larger, y gets closer to zero', you can say 'as x tends to infinity, y tends to zero'

In mathematical notation this is: $\lim\limits_{x \to \infty} y(x) = 0$

This is read as 'the limit of y, as x tends to infinity, equals zero'.

▶ If a graph approaches closer and closer to a line without touching it, that line is an **asymptote** to the graph

In graph B, the x-axis is a **horizontal asymptote** to $y = e^{-x}$

In graph F, the line $y = 5$ is a horizontal asymptote to $y = 5 - 2e^{\,0.5x}$

Example 9

Sketch the graph of $y = 16 + 64e^{-0.065t}$ for $t \geq 0$, showing any asymptotes and axis intercepts.

When $t = 0$, $y = 16 + 64 \times 1 = 80$

As $t \to \infty$, $e^{-0.065t} \to 0$

So $y \to 16$

The line $y = 16$ is an asymptote.

> See also example **5**.
> 16 °C is the temperature of the room.

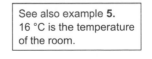

> ► All **logarithmic graphs** have the same basic shape as $y = \log_2 x$

Here are two logarithmic graphs, with the intercepts and asymptotes shown. The first graph also has $y = e^x$ (the inverse function of $y = \ln x$) shown as a dotted line.

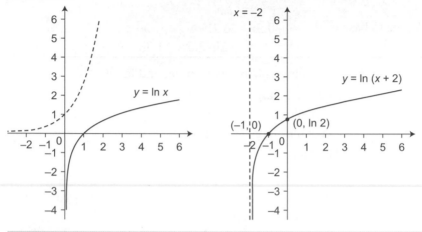

> ► Logarithmic graphs have vertical asymptotes
> ► Exponential graphs have horizontal asymptotes

Example 10

Show why the axis intercepts of the graph of $y = \ln(x + 2)$ have the values shown in the diagram.

- -

y-axis is $x = 0$ x-axis is $y = 0$

$y = \ln(0+2)$ $\ln(x + 2) = 0$ raising e to the power

$\quad = \ln 2$ $x + 2 = e^0 = 1$ of both sides

The graph meets the $x = -1$

y-axis at $(0, \ln 2)$ The graph meets the x-axis at $(-1, 0)$

Exercise 5.3

1 Match the graph to the equation.

a) $y = e^{0.5x}$

b) $y = 0.5e^x$

c) $y = 0.5e^{-x}$

d) $y = 2 - e^{-x}$

e) $y = 2 - e^x$

f) $y = 2 + 3e^{-0.5x}$

g) $y = \ln x + 2$

h) $y = -\ln x$

i) $y = \ln(x + e)$

The graph of $y = e^x$ is shown as a dotted line.

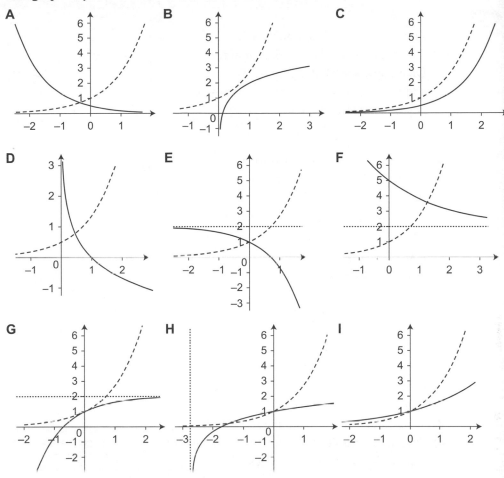

2 **a)** Sketch the graphs of the functions in Exercise **5.1**, questions **5** and **6** for $t \geq 0$, showing any intercepts with the axes and any asymptotes.

  b) What happens to y in each case as $t \to \infty$?

  c) What happens to the *gradient* of the graph in each case as $t \to \infty$?

3 Use a computer or your calculator to draw each of the following graphs. For each graph, write down the equations of any (horizontal or vertical) asymptotes.

  a) $y = \dfrac{1}{x}$

  b) $y = \dfrac{1}{x^2}$

  c) $y = \dfrac{1}{x+2}$

  d) $y = \dfrac{1}{x} + 3$

  e) $y = \dfrac{1}{x-4} + 5$

  f) $y = \dfrac{5}{x-3}$

4 a) If the function f is defined for $x \geq 2$ by

p.102

$$f(x) = \sqrt{x-2}$$

Find the inverse function $f^{-1}(x)$

b) The graph of $y = f(x)$ is shown here. On a copy, sketch the graphs of $y = f(x)$ and $y = f^{-1}(x)$ on the same axes, showing any axis intercepts.

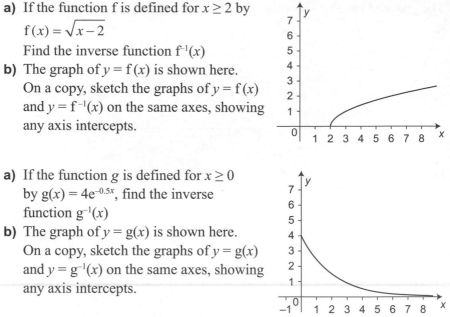

5 a) If the function g is defined for $x \geq 0$ by $g(x) = 4e^{-0.5x}$, find the inverse function $g^{-1}(x)$

b) The graph of $y = g(x)$ is shown here. On a copy, sketch the graphs of $y = g(x)$ and $y = g^{-1}(x)$ on the same axes, showing any axis intercepts.

6 A dish of food is removed from a hot oven and left to cool in a room. The temperature, y °C, of the dish when it has been out of the oven for t minutes can be modelled by the equation $y = 20 + 175e^{-0.08t}$

a) Find the initial temperature when it comes out of the oven.

b) Find the temperature after 11 minutes.

c) After how long is the temperature 60 °C?

d) What happens to the temperature in the long term?

e) Sketch the graph of y against t, showing any axis intercepts and asymptotes.

> If asked to *sketch* a graph, just show the main features.

7 Sketch the following graphs, showing any axis intercepts and asymptotes.

a) $y = \ln(x + 1)$ **b)** $y = 2 - \ln x$

c) $y = e^x - 2$ **d)** $y = 3e^{-x} - 4$

8 The total number of views of a video on YouTube is 200 at 12 noon on Friday. The number of views then doubles every 5 hours.

The number of views, N, at time t hours after 12 noon on Friday can be modelled by a function of the form $N = Ae^{kt}$ for $0 \leq t \leq 50$, where A and k are constants.

a) Write down the value of A.

b) By substituting $t = 5$ and $N = 400$ in $N = Ae^{kt}$, find the value of the constant k.

c) Use your equation to find the number of views at 10 a.m. on Saturday.

d) Draw the graph of N against t for $0 \leq t \leq 15$

> If asked to *draw* a graph, plot some points.

9 The number of bats, N, on an island can be modelled by the equation $N = 15\,000 - 12\,000e^{-0.135t}$, where t is the number of years since observations began.

a) Use the equation to complete the table below.

t (years)	0	5	10	15	20
N bats	3000	8890			

b) Draw the graph of N against t.

Use a horizontal scale for values of t from 0 to 20, with 2 cm representing 5 years.

Use a vertical scale for values of N from 0 to 16 000, with 2 cm representing 2000 bats.

c) Describe what happens to the number of bats as $t \to \infty$

d) Find the gradient of the tangent when $t = 7$

e) State the units of the gradient.

f) Explain the meaning of the gradient.

g) Describe what happens to the gradient as $t \to \infty$

Use *Disease* on Data Sheet **5**

10 A model for the number of people, N, who have been infected is given by the equation $N = 400 - 300e^{-0.1t}$

where t is the number of days since records of the disease were started.

a) i) Using the model, complete a copy of this table of values.

t	0	10	20	30	40
N	100				395

(2 marks)

ii) Using a time scale from 0 to 40 days and an N scale from 0 to 400, draw the graph of the equation
$N = 400 - 300e^{-0.1t}$ for $0 \leq t \leq 40$ *(3 marks)*

b) When does the model predict that the value of N will be 398?

(2 marks)

c) What is the maximum value of N predicted by this model?

(1 mark)

(AQA 2010)

Non-linear laws

You saw earlier how a line of best fit can be used to fit a linear function to a set of data. This process is harder when the data are related in a non-linear way. Fortunately, you can sometimes transform a non-linear model to a linear one.

p.18

The table shows the monthly sales, y thousands, of a mobile phone x months after the start of an advertising campaign.

x	1	2	3	4	5	6
y	25	28	36	50	65	87

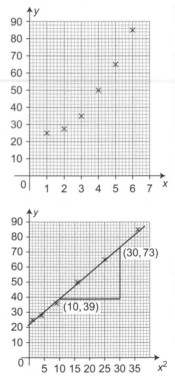

Plotting the data on a graph, you see that it looks approximately quadratic. You want to see if you can fit the data to a function of the form $y = ax^2 + b$. One way to do this is to square all the x-values and draw up a new table.

x^2	1	4	9	16	25	36
y	25	28	36	50	65	87

Now plot y against x^2. This is approximately a straight line, so y and x^2 have a linear relationship and the model $y = ax^2 + b$ is appropriate. Draw a line of best fit.

Intercept $\quad b = 22$

Gradient $\quad a = \dfrac{\Delta y}{\Delta x} = \dfrac{73 - 39}{30 - 10} = \dfrac{34}{20} = 1.7$

A suitable model for the data is $y = 1.7x^2 + 22$

In some other cases, you can use **logarithms** to convert from a non-linear to a linear relationship. The table shows the height y metres of a tree at age x years.

x	1	2	3	4	5
y	1.43	2.47	3.20	3.75	4.34

You think it might be possible to model the height by a **power law** of the form $y = ax^b$, where a and b are constants.

To transform this to a linear equation, take logs to base e of both sides.

$\ln y = \ln (ax^b)$

$\ln y = \ln a + \ln (x^b)$ | Using the first then third laws of logs.

$\ln y = \ln a + b \ln x$

> ► If $y = ax^b$ then $\ln y = \ln a + b \ln x$

Make a table of values of $\ln x$ and $\ln y$.

ln x	0	0.69	1.10	1.39	1.61
ln y	0.36	0.90	1.16	1.32	1.47

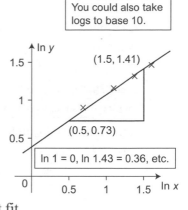

You could also take logs to base 10.

(1.5, 1.41)

(0.5, 0.73)

ln 1 = 0, ln 1.43 = 0.36, etc.

Draw a graph of $\ln y$ against $\ln x$. This is approximately a straight line. Draw a line of best fit.

Intercept $\ln a = 0.39$

$a = e^{0.39} = 1.48$

Gradient $b = \dfrac{\Delta y}{\Delta x} = \dfrac{1.41 - 0.73}{1.5 - 0.5} = \dfrac{0.68}{1} = 0.68$

A suitable model for the data is $y = 1.48x^{0.68}$

Taking logs also works if your model is an **exponential function.**

Anton records the weight y grams of a culture in a Petri dish at time x hours.

x	12	24	36	48	60
y	27.1	37.3	55.2	75.8	111

He thinks the data can be modelled by an exponential function of the form $y = ka^x$, where k and a are constants. Take logs to base e of both sides.

$\ln y = \ln (ka^x)$

$\ln y = \ln k + \ln (a^x)$ | Using the first then third laws of logs.

$\ln y = \ln k + x \ln a$

> ► If $y = ka^x$ then $\ln y = \ln k + x \ln a$

(50, 4.42)

(10, 3.22)

Make a table of x (not $\ln x$) and $\ln y$.

x	12	24	36	48	60
ln y	3.30	3.62	4.01	4.33	4.71

Intercept $\ln k = 2.92$

$k = e^{2.92} = 18.5$

Gradient $\ln a = \dfrac{\Delta y}{\Delta x} = \dfrac{4.42 - 3.22}{50 - 10} = 0.03$

$a = e^{0.03} = 1.03$

A suitable model for the data is $y = 18.5(1.03^x)$

Check by substituting the original data.

Exercise 5.4

1 The Highway Code includes a chart of 'Typical Stopping Distances' which show how long it would take a car to stop from a given speed in good driving conditions.

Speed, x (miles per hour)	20	30	40	50	60	70
Stopping distance, y (metres)	12	23	36	53	73	96

It is thought that a suitable model for these data is a function of the form $y = ax^2 + b$, where a and b are constants.

a) Complete a copy of the table.

x^2	400					
y	12	23	36	53	73	96

b) Draw a graph of y against x^2.

c) Draw a line of best fit on your graph and use it to estimate the constants a and b.

d) Substitute a and b into the equation $y = ax^2 + b$. Use your equation to estimate the stopping distance for a car travelling at 35 mph.

e) Solve your equation to estimate the speed of a car with a stopping distance of 60 metres.

2 The amount of a radioactive isotope present decreases with time. Anton records the amount, y grams, remaining t days after an experiment.

t	1	2	3	4	5	6
y	200	159	129	105	88	71

It is thought that the data can be modelled by an equation of the form $y = 200a^t$ where a is a constant.

a) Express $\ln y$ in terms of t.

b) Complete a copy of the table.

t	1	2	3	4	5	6
$\ln y$						

c) Draw a graph of $\ln y$ against t.

d) Draw a line of best fit on your graph. Use your line to estimate the constant a.

Your line should pass through the point (0, ln 200). Why?

e) Substitute a into the equation $y = 200a^t$. Use your equation to estimate the amount of the isotope remaining after 8 days.

f) Solve your equation to estimate how long it takes for the amount to reduce to 25 g.

Use *Bacteria* on Data Sheet **5**

3 The number of bacteria, N, can be modelled by the equation
$N = kt^c$ where t is the number of hours since the start of the experiment,
and k and c are both constants.

a) For this model, show that $\ln N = \ln k + c \ln t$.   (*1 mark*)

b) Complete the table of values for $\ln t$ and $\ln N$,
giving the values to 3 significant figures.

t	1	2	3	4	5	6
N	70	390	1100	2240	3900	6200
$\ln t$						
$\ln N$						

(*2 marks*)

c) Use a grid, with $\ln t$ from 0 to 1.8 and $\ln N$ from 0 to 9.0,
to plot $\ln N$ against $\ln t$.
Draw a line of best fit on your diagram.   (*2 marks*)

d) Find the equation for the line of best fit in terms of
$\ln N$ and $\ln t$.   (*3 marks*)

e) Hence express N in terms of t.   (*2 marks*)

(AQA 2006)

Use *Trees* on Data Sheet **5**

4 The equation $y = ax^2 + b$, where a and b are constants, can be used to
model the height, y cm, of a fir tree in terms of the circumference, x cm.

a) Complete a copy of the table of values.

Circumference, x (cm)	10	38	55	68	81	94
x^2						
Height, y (cm)	130	260	440	580	760	1000

(*2 marks*)

b) Use a grid with x^2 from 0 to 9000 and y from 0 to 1200, to plot y
against x^2. Draw a line of best fit on your graph.   (*3 marks*)

c) Use your graph to predict the height of a fir tree with
circumference 60 cm.   (*2 marks*)

d) Use your graph to predict the circumference of a fir tree
with height 300 cm.   (*2 marks*)

(AQA 2006)

Investigation – exponential functions and non-linear laws

It is often claimed that exponential or logarithmic curves are found in nature. For example, logarithmic spirals are said to occur in nautilus shells, the swirls of hurricanes and the bands of spiral galaxies. This means that the radius of the curve, r, is related to the angle, θ, turned through from a fixed direction by

$$r = ae^{b\theta} \quad \Leftrightarrow \quad \theta = \frac{1}{b}\ln\left(\frac{r}{a}\right)$$

1 Find examples of where exponentials or logarithms are used to model natural phenomena.

Zipf's law is an empirical observation about the relative frequency of words in a written language. For the nth most popular word,

relative frequency $= \dfrac{a}{n^b}$

where a and b are constants.

It is an example of the application of power laws to statistics. Similar laws have been proposed for many other applications in economics, sociology and computer science where data can be placed in rank order.

Often it is found numerically that the exponent, $b \approx 1.16$ This gives rise to the 'Pareto principle', 80% of the effects come from 20% of the causes. Applied to income distributions, it says 20% of the population controls 80% of the wealth. It was even claimed by Zipf that a significant deviation from this distribution of income inequality can predict a revolution.

2 Find examples of where rank order is used to describe the distribution of data.

Research

Power laws and exponential laws are very common in the sciences. What forms are taken by the following laws: Kepler's third, Moore's, Coulomb's, Malthus', Stefan-Boltzmann, Kleiber's, Steven's, Beer-Lambert?

What other examples of power laws and exponential laws can you find?

How do you decide between the two types of mathematical law?

Power law: $y = ax^b$ **Exponential law**: $y = ab^x$

'x raised to a power'   'a base raised to the power x'

3   Show that $y = ab^x$ can be written $y = ae^{(\ln b)x}$

4   By taking logs of both sides show that you can rewrite the laws as

Power: $\log y = \log a + b \log x$
Exponential: $\log y = \log a + x \log b$

To test if your data has a power law or an exponential law plot both $\log y$ against $\log x$ (a log-log plot) and $\log y$ against x (a log-linear plot) and decide which, if any, graph can best be described by a straight line. By adding a line of best fit 'by eye' you can use your estimates of the intercept and gradient to determine a and b and thus fix the equation.

ICT opportunity

Use a spread sheet or similar program to draw graphs of your data and to fit a straight-line to the points.

The module Data Analysis discusses a method to find a line of best fit and to quantify how well it fits the data.

It is also possible that for one range of the data a log-linear plot works best – an exponential law – and for another range a log-log plot works best – a power law.

Project

Select a set of data which is of interest to you and which you think might be modelled using either an exponential or a power law. By drawing suitable graphs test your ideas. How well does your model work and over what range?

Consolidation

You should now be able to
- Find a multiplier and use it to set up an exponential equation
- Substitute into exponential equations to solve practical problems
- Use logarithms, including ln, to solve exponential equations
- Find inverse functions algebraically
- Sketch graphs of inverse functions
- Sketch the graph of $y = f(-x)$ given the graph of $y = f(x)$
- Sketch and identify graphs of exponential and log functions
- Find asymptotes and axis intercepts
- Complete tables of exponential and log functions
- Transform the function $y = ax^2 + b$ to linear form and draw a graph to find a and b
- Transform the function $y = ax^b$ to linear form, by taking logs, and draw a graph of ln y against ln x to find a and b
- Transform the function $y = ka^x$ to linear form, by taking logs, and draw a graph of ln y against x to find k and a
- Distinguish between power and exponential models by taking logs and drawing graphs

Use *Newton's law of cooling* on Data Sheet **5**

1 a) John's kitchen is at a temperature of 20 °C. He makes a cup of tea with boiling water at 100 °C. Five minutes later the temperature of the cup of tea is 75 °C. The temperature of the cup of tea, T °C, x minutes after being made is given by the equation
$T = 20 + 80e^{-kx}$
where k is a positive constant.
  i) Sketch the graph of T against x on a copy of the axes.
          (2 marks)
  ii) The information given above leads to the equation $55 = 80e^{-5k}$
          Calculate the value of k. *(3 marks)*

b) The temperature of a cup of coffee made in another kitchen is given by the equation $T = 15 + 80e^{-0.1x}$
  i) What is the temperature in this kitchen? *(1 mark)*
  ii) What is the initial temperature of the cup of coffee? *(1 mark)*
  iii) Use this model to calculate the temperature of the cup of coffee after 10 minutes. *(2 marks)*

(AQA 2011)

Use *Energy consumption* on Data Sheet **5**

2 a) A model for the energy consumption, E million tons of coal, at time t years after 1960 is $E = 300e^{0.036658t}$
  i) Use this model to calculate the energy consumption in 2010. *(2 marks)*

  ii) Use this model to calculate when the energy consumption is expected to be 2500 million tons of coal. *(3 marks)*

b) Another model for the energy consumption, E million tons of coal, at time t years after 1960 is $E = 6.5527t^{1.507829}$
  i) Use this model to calculate the energy consumption in 2010. *(2 marks)*

  ii) Use this model to calculate when the energy consumption is expected to be 2500 million tons of coal. *(3 marks)*
  iii) Explain why it is a poor model near 1960. *(1 mark)*

c) The graphs of the models $E = 300e^{0.036658t}$ and $E = 6.5527t^{1.507829}$ are given below.

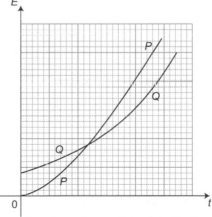

The graphs intersect when $t = 21.1$ and are labelled P and Q.
Explain which graph represents the model $E = 300e^{0.036658t}$ *(2 marks)*

(AQA 2009)

Use *Life expectancy* on Data Sheet **5**

3 a) A possible model for the life expectancy, y years, at age x years is given by the equation

$$y = 75e^{\left(-\frac{x}{50}\right)}$$

Use this model to find:

i) the life expectancy at age 60 years; *(2 marks)*

ii) the age at which the life expectancy is 30 years. *(3 marks)*

b) A second model for the life expectancy is given by the equation

$$y = 76 - x$$

Why is this model not appropriate for ages greater than 76 years?

(1 mark)

c) i) Sketch the graph of $y = \frac{k}{x}$ where k is a positive constant.

(1 mark)

ii) Why is this **not** a suitable model to use for life expectancy?

(2 marks)

(AQA 2006)

Use *Computer speeds* on Data Sheet **5**

4 The computing speed, S operations per second, can be modelled by the equation

$$S = ka^t$$

where t is the number of years since 1972 and a and k are constants.

a) Complete a copy of the table of values.

t	0	10	21	31	35
S	3.5×10^3	1.34×10^5	5.5×10^6	8.4×10^7	4×10^8
ln S					

(2 marks)

b) On a grid with t from 0 to 35 and ln S from 0 to 20, plot ln S against t.

Draw a line of best fit on your graph. *(3 marks)*

c) Find the equation for the line of best fit in terms of ln S and t. *(3 marks)*

d) Hence express S in terms of t. *(2 marks)*

(AQA 2011)

Use *Earthquakes* on Data Sheet **5**.

5 The energy, E joules, released by an earthquake of magnitude r on the
Richter scale can be modelled by the equation
$$E = k \times a^r$$
where k and a are constants.

a) For this model, show that $\ln E = \ln k + r \ln a$. *(1 mark)*

b) Complete a copy of the table of values, giving
the values of $\ln E$ to three significant figures.

r	1	2	3	4	5	6	7
E	1.34×10^8	4.20×10^9	1.34×10^{11}	4.20×10^{12}	1.34×10^{14}	4.20×10^{15}	1.34×10^{17}
$\ln E$							

(2 marks)

c) i) Use a grid with r from 0 to 7 and $\ln E$ from 0 to 40,
to plot $\ln E$ against r.
Draw a line of best fit on your graph. *(2 marks)*

ii) Use your graph to find the values of k and a. *(3 marks)*

d) How much energy is released by an earthquake of magnitude 10 on the
Richter scale? Give your answer in standard form. *(1 mark)*

e) What is the number on the Richter scale that corresponds with an
earthquake that releases 4.2×10^7 joules of energy? *(2 marks)*

(AQA 2010)

Data sheet 1

Vintage clothing

Anita and Seth have a shop which
sells vintage clothing from the
years 1940 to 1990.

They buy most of their stock from
wholesalers. These wholesalers sell
some grades of clothes in bulk at a
fixed price per kilogram. In some
cases they add a fixed delivery charge.

Babies

The ages and weights of a sample of 10 babies at a post-natal clinic are
recorded.

Age (weeks)	1	3	5	5	6	7	9	10	12	14
Weight (kg)	3.1	3.8	4.2	3.7	4.1	4.8	4.6	4.9	5.7	5.4

Plumbers

Many plumbers have a labour charge which is made up of two parts: a fixed
callout charge and a charge per hour.

If a plumber works for x hours, and the customer pays £y for labour, the
plumber uses the equation $y = ax + b$ to calculate how much to charge the
customer for labour.

Fuel consumption

In a survey of cars with petrol engines, it was found that in general the
greater the mass of a car the fewer miles it travelled per gallon.
Some of the results are shown below.

Mass (kg)	2306	1050	880	2500	1250	1550	1770	1750	2100	1000
Fuel consumption (mpg)	20	47	46	17	42	36	25	30	23	45

Data sheet 2

Skateboard ramps

Errol and Ji are designing a range of skateboard ramps. As well as making prototypes of the ramps, they want to model them for a virtual skateboarding game. For these purposes, they are planning to model the ramps with quadratic functions.

Receivers

The Lovell telescope at Jodrell Bank is used to receive radio waves from the universe. It can move in three dimensions.

The diameter of the bowl is 76 metres. The height of the axis of rotation of the bowl is 50 metres.

Wembley stadium

The roof of Wembley stadium is supported by an arch that has a span of 315 metres. The arch has a maximum vertical height of 133 metres above ground level.

Ticket sales

Tickets are sold at a pop concert. The graph shows the number of tickets sold each day up to the date of the concert.

Income

When selling items, it is often found that the higher the selling price, £x, the lower the demand, d.
The income, £I, is found by multiplying the selling price by the demand.

Big dipper

This graph shows part of a fun fair ride.

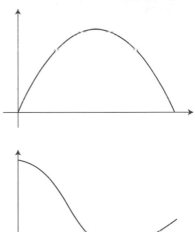

Data sheet 3

Falmouth tides

The graph shows the height of the tide in Falmouth at different times (given in GMT, not BST) on 19th April 2012.

Zoë is a marine biologist. She wants to see if she can model the height of the tide using sine or cosine functions.

She also wants to find the rate of change of the height of the tide at different times.

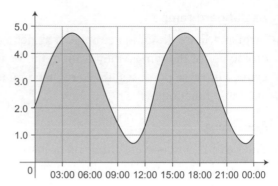

Fairground

A fairground ride consists of seats fastened onto a big wheel.

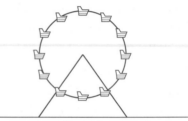

Ground

Temperature

The average temperature in Yakutsk in Russia is 42 °C at the start of each year. It rises to 18 °C by the middle of the year.

Blyth tides

The graph shows the height of the tide during a 24-hour period in Blyth harbour.

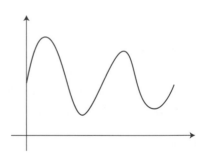

Sunrise

The graph shows how the time of sunrise in Durham varies during a period of one year. Time refers to Greenwich Mean Time. The weeks start on 21st September.

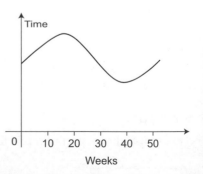

Data sheet 4

Sound engineer

Hannah is learning to be a sound engineer. She is responsible for hiring and organising the sound system needed for an outdoor gig. She needs to be confident that the music will be audible at quite a great distance from the stage.

Hannah uses a model which states that the sound intensity at a given distance from the sound source follows an inverse square law.

Data sheet 5

Laboratory technician

Anton is a lab technician. He notices that in some processes, such as cooling and the growth of biological cultures, there is a quantity that either doubles or halves in a fixed period of time.

Anton wants to find equations to model these processes.

Disease

The inhabitants of a small town are suffering from a disease.
The number of infected people is recorded, but only after the disease has already infected some of the inhabitants.

Time (days)	0	10	20	30	40
Number who have been infected	100	260	340	370	395

Bacteria

In an experiment, the number of bacteria is recorded every hour.

Hour	1	2	3	4	5	6
Number of bacteria	70	390	1100	2240	3900	6200

Trees

The table shows the heights and circumferences of some fir trees.

Circumference (cm)	10	38	55	68	81	94
Height (cm)	130	260	440	580	760	1000

Newton's law of cooling

This states that the rate of change of temperature of an object is proportional to the difference in temperature between the object and its surroundings.

Energy consumption

The energy consumption per year of Chinese industry was measured in millions of tons of coal.

Year	1960	1980	2000	2004
Energy consumption	300	600	1300	1970

Life expectancy

The life expectancy of a person is the number of *further* years that they are expected to live.

For example, a man who has reached the age of 55 years can expect to live a *further* 24 years.

The table shows the life expectancy at various ages for males in Europe.

Age	Life expectancy
5	71
15	61
25	51
35	41
45	33
55	24
65	16
75	9
85	5
95	3

Computer speeds

The average number of operations performed per second (speed) by computer processors is recorded each year.

The results for some years are shown in the table below.

Year	1972	1982	1993	2003	2007
Speed	3.5×10^3	1.34×10^5	5.5×10^6	8.4×10^7	4×10^8

Earthquakes

The magnitude of an earthquake is measured by a number on the Richter scale.

The energy released by an earthquake increases by a factor of 1000 for every increase of two in the reading on the Richter scale.

Practice paper 1 – data sheet

Bicycle sales

A factory makes different models of bicycle.

The monthly profit from making and selling bicycles can be expressed as a quadratic function of the number of bicycles made and sold in that month.

Body temperature

The temperature of the human body varies in a 24-hour cycle.

It is lowest at around 6.00 a.m. and highest at around 6.00 p.m.

Crumpled paper

Researchers have studied pieces of crumpled-up paper which have been thrown into waste-paper bins. It is thought that the mass of a piece of crumpled-up paper can be related to its diameter by a power law of the form $m = kd^c$, where k and c are constants.

Practice paper 1 – questions

SECTION A
Use *Bicycle sales* on the Data Sheet

1 The profit £P from making and selling x 'HighBreed' bicycles
   can be modelled by the equation $P = -x^2 + 130x - 3000$
   a) Express P in the form $P = -(x + r)^2 + q$
      where r and q are constants   *(3 marks)*
   b) Find the greatest possible profit.   *(1 mark)*
   c) Find the number of bicycles that must be sold to
      make this profit.   *(1 mark)*
   d) Find the number of bicycles made and sold if the profit
      is zero (these are known as the break-even points).   *(2 marks)*

2 The monthly profit £P from making and selling x
   'Trail Man' bicycles can be modelled by an equation
   of the form $P = -(x + m)^2 + n$ where m and n are constants.
   The greatest possible profit is £1620, and this profit is made
   when 52 'Trail Man' bicycles are made and sold.
   a) Find the values of the constants m and n, and hence express
      P in the form $P = -x^2 + bx + c$ where b and c are constants.   *(4 marks)*
   b) Find the profit when 40 bicycles are made and sold.   *(1 mark)*
   c) Find the numbers of bicycles that could be made and sold
      if the monthly profit is £1000.   *(3 marks)*

SECTION B
Use *Body temperature* on the Data Sheet

3 A person's body temperature y °C has a maximum value of 37.3 at 6:00
   p.m. and a minimum value of 36.7 at 6:00 a.m. It can be modelled by an
   equation of the form
   $y = A \cos(kt)° + c$
   where t is the number of hours after 6.00 p.m. and A, k and c
   are constants.
   a) Find the values of the constants A, k and c.   *(4 marks)*

b) Find the temperature predicted by the model at 11:00 p.m.
Give your answer to two decimal places. *(2 marks)*

c) Find the values of t at which the temperature would be 36.8 °C
according to the model. *(3 marks)*

d) Write down an equation that could be used to model the body
temperature if t is the number of hours after **midnight** instead of the
number of hours after 6.00 p.m. *(1 mark)*

SECTION C
Use *Crumpled paper* on the Data Sheet

4 It is thought that the mass m grams of a piece of crumpled-up paper can be
related to its diameter d cm by a power law of the form $m = kd^c$, where
k and c are constants.
The table shows data relating to some pieces of crumpled paper.

d	2	2.6	3.8	5.2	8.9
m	2.3	4.4	11.0	25.1	93.6

a) Use the laws of logs to transform the equation $m = kd^c$
into an equation expressing $\ln m$ in terms of $\ln d$. *(2 marks)*

b) Complete a copy of the table.

ln d	0.69				
ln m	0.83				

(2 marks)

c) Draw a graph of $\ln m$ against $\ln d$. *(3 marks)*

d) Draw a line of best fit on your graph and use it to
estimate the constants c and k. *(4 marks)*

e) Substitute c and k into the equation $m = kd^c$.
Use your equation to estimate the mass of a crumpled
piece of paper of diameter 12 cm. *(2 marks)*

f) Solve your equation to estimate the diameter of a
crumpled piece of paper of mass 42 g. *(2 marks)*

Practice paper 2 – data sheet

BMX trail

A trail for BMX bikes has a series of small, steep hills on it.
Different mathematical models can be used to represent these hills.

Frozen food

Some frozen foods need to be defrosted before they can be cooked.
The temperature of an item at a certain time after it is removed from a freezer
can be modelled by an exponential function.

Human population

The world's human population reached 1 billion (1×10^9) around 1830.
By 1950 this had more than doubled and by 2010 it was approaching
7 billion.

Practice paper 2 – questions

SECTION A
Use *BMX trail* on the Data Sheet

1   A hill on a BMX trail is modelled by the equation $y = 0.9x - 0.3x^2$, where
    x metres is the horizontal distance and y metres is the height, measured
    from a fixed point O.
    a) Find the horizontal distance from O where the hill is
       next at the same height as O.   *(2 marks)*
    b) The model is considered valid if $y \geq 0$.
       By finding the values of y for $x = 0, 0.5, 1, 1.5$ etc.,
       draw the graph of $y = 0.9x - 0.3x^2$ for $y \geq 0$.   *(4 marks)*
    c) Why would the model not be suitable for much greater
       values of x?   *(1 mark)*

2   The same hill as in Question **1** could also be modelled by the equation
    $y = 0.675 \sin (60x)°$, where x metres is the horizontal distance and
    y metres is the height, measured from a fixed point O.
    a) Complete the table below.

x	0	0.5	1	1.5	2	2.5	3	3.5	4	4.5	5	5.5	6
y	0	0.338											

                                                                        (2 marks)
    b) Draw the graph of $y = 0.675 \sin (60x)°$ for $0 \leq 0\ x \leq 6$ *(3 marks)*
    c) How does this graph differ from the graph you drew in
       Question 1?   *(1 mark)*
    d) By drawing a tangent, estimate the gradient of the track
       at a horizontal distance of 2.4 metres from O.   *(2 marks)*

SECTION B
Use *Frozen foods* on the Data Sheet

3   A frozen pizza is removed from a freezer and left in a room. Its
    temperature y °C when it has been out of the freezer for t minutes can be
    modelled by the equation $y = 19 - 30e^{-0.004t}$.

a) What is the temperature of the pizza immediately after it is taken from the freezer? *(1 mark)*

b) What is the temperature of the room? *(1 mark)*

c) Find the temperature of the pizza 1 hour after it is taken from the freezer. *(2 marks)*

d) How many minutes after the pizza is taken from the freezer is its temperature 0°C? *(3 marks)*

e) Sketch the graph of $y = 19 - 30e^{-0.004t}$ for $t \geq 0$, showing any axis intercepts and asymptotes. *(4 marks)*

SECTION C

Use *Human population* on the Data Sheet

4 The world's human population reached 1 billion (1×10^9) around 1830. The table shows an estimate of the total population, P millions, at 30-year intervals since then.

Year	1830	1860	1890	1920	1950
P	1000	1200	1500	1800	2400

The data can be modelled by a function of the form $P = ka^t$, where t is the number of years since 1830.

a) Use the laws of logs to express ln P in terms of t. *(2 marks)*

b) Complete a copy of the table.

t	0	30	60	90	120
ln P	6.91				

(2 marks)

c) Draw a graph of ln P against t *(3 marks)*

d) Add a line of best fit and use it to estimate the constants a and k. *(4 marks)*

e) Substitute a and k into the equation $P = ka^t$. Use your equation to estimate the world population in 1980 if the model continues to be valid. *(2 marks)*

f) Suggest a reason why this model might not be valid for all of the next 100 years. *(1 mark)*

Answers

Chapter 1
Preparation 1

1 **a)** $10x + 15 + 12x - 2 = 22x + 13$

   b) $3x - 12 - 12x + 20 = -9x + 8$

   c) $-6x - 8y - 15 + 6x - 6y = -14y - 15$

2 $2y = 6 - 3x \Rightarrow y = 3 - 1.5x$

3 $2x - y = 20 \Rightarrow 2x - 20 = y$

4 **a, b)**

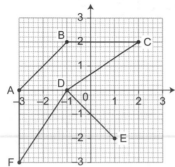

5 $y = 5 - 2x$; 9, 5, 1, –3

6

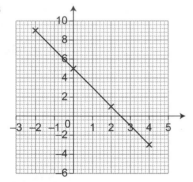

All points lie on a straight line.

Exercise 1.1

1 **a)** $k = \dfrac{81}{6} = 13.5 \Rightarrow y = 13.5x$

   b) $13.5 \times 4.2 = £56.70$ **c)** $k = \dfrac{32}{13.5} = 2.37\,\text{kg}$

2 a, c, f

3 **a)** **i)** $\dfrac{15}{4.5} = 3.75$ **ii)** $\dfrac{76}{20} = 3.8$

   b) **ii)** OB because it is longer than OA

4 **a)** $y = 1.6x$ **b)** $x = 0.625y$

   c) Reciprocals: $1.6 \times 0.625 = 1$

6 AB 3, CD $\dfrac{1}{4}$, EF –1, GH 0, IJ $-\dfrac{2}{3}$

7 **a)** 8, 3   **b)** –4, 6   **c)** –7, 5   **d)** 1.25, –1.5

8 **a)** 10   **b)** 20

c)

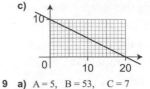

d) –0.5

9 **a)** A = 5, B = 53, C = 7

   b) A = –8, B = 1000, C = 12

   c) A = 12, B = 8, C = 2

10 **a)** $y = 12x + 5$; $y = 2x - 8$; $y = -1.5x + 12$

   b) £ per day; °C per hour; metres per second per second

11 x = constant: vertical line, gradient is undefined or infinite y = constant: horizontal line, $m = 0$

12 **a)** $m = \dfrac{1}{3}$, $c = 4$; $y = \dfrac{1}{3}x + 4$

   b) $m = 1.6$, $c = -6$; $y = 1.6x - 6$

   c) $m = -1$, $c = -2$; $y = -x - 2$

13 **a)** $m = \dfrac{1-8}{5-3} = -3.5$ **b)** $m = \dfrac{15-5}{-6+9} = \dfrac{10}{3} \cong 3.33$

   c) $m = \dfrac{11+5}{-4} = -4$ **d)** $m = \dfrac{-5-3}{-4+2} = 4$

14 $m = \dfrac{3-27}{19-11} = -3$, $27 = -3 \times 11 + c \Rightarrow c = 60$

   $y = -3x + 60$

Exercise 1.2

1 **a)** $x = 3.5, y = 32$

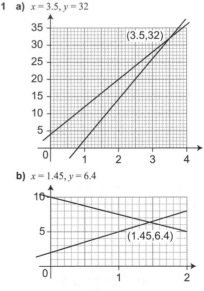

   b) $x = 1.45, y = 6.4$

2 **a)** $0.5x - 18 = 12 - 2x$

   $2.5x = 30 \Rightarrow x = 12$, $y = -12$

   b) $12x - 2(4x - 7) = 32$

   $4x = 18 \Rightarrow x = 4.5$, $y = 11$

3 **a)** Subtract: $3x = -12 \Rightarrow x = -4$, $y = 7$

   b) Subtract: $3y = 9 \Rightarrow y = 3$, $x = 1$

c) Subtract: $3y = 12 \Rightarrow y = 4$, $x = 3$
d) Add: $8x = 40 \Rightarrow x = 5$, $y = 1$
e) $4x - 6y = 40$
Add: $9x = 63 \Rightarrow x = 7$, $y = -2$
f) $6x + 15y = 6$ and $6x - 8y = 98$
Subtract: $23y = -92 \Rightarrow y = -4$, $x = 11$

4 a) $y = 2.25x + 30$
b) As section **2.1** with extra line $y = 2.25x + 30$
c) i) $2.25x + 30 - 2.4x \to x - 200$, $y - 480$
ii) $2.25x + 30 = 2.2x + 42 \Rightarrow x = 240$, $y = 570$
d) $x < 200$ Funny Valentines;
$200 < x < 240$ Peppers; $x > 240$ Tramps

5 a) YC: $y = 0.7x + 4$;
Trans: $y = 0.9x + 2.5$
b) $0.9x + 2.5 = 0.7x + 4 \Rightarrow 0.2x = 1.5$
$x = 7.5$, $y = 9.25$
c) Equal costs (£9.25) for 7.5 miles.

6 a) £1500   **b)** 3.2   **c)** £per T-shirt
d)

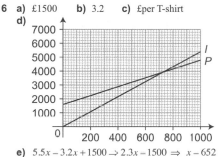

e) $5.5x - 3.2x + 1500 \to 2.3x - 1500 \Rightarrow x - 652$

7 x pence = cost of a can of cola,
y pence = cost of a packet of crisps
$4x + 5y = 350 \Rightarrow 32x + 40y = 2800$
$11x + 8y = 698$ $55x + 40y = 3490$
$23x = 690 \Rightarrow x = 30$, $y = 46$
Cola costs 30p, crisps cost 46p.

8 a) x – number of aliens, y – no. of bears eyes.
$x + 2y = 2000$ and $5x + 4y = 6400$
b) $2x + 4y = 4000 \Rightarrow x = 800$, $y = 600$
c) They make 800 aliens and 600 bears

Exercise 1.3
1 a)

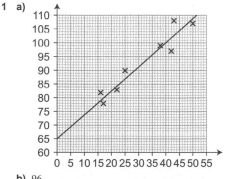

b) 96

2 a) $m = 0.7$, $c = -0.9 \Rightarrow y = 0.7x - 0.9$
b) $y = 0.7 \times 5 - 0.9 = 2.6$; £2.6m profit
c) The company makes a loss

3 a)

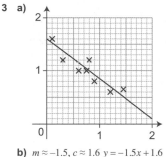

b) $m \approx -1.5$, $c \approx 1.6$ $y = -1.5x + 1.6$
c) $y = -1.5 \times 0.5 + 1.6 = €0.85$

Investigation 1
1

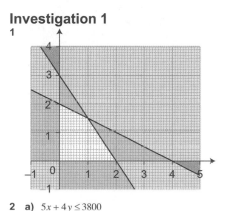

2 a) $5x + 4y \leq 3800$
b)

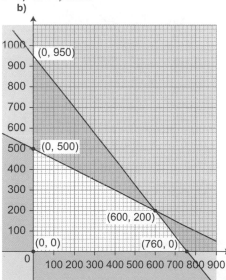

3 a) $P = 9x + 6y$
b, c)

Vertex	P = 9x + 6y	P = 8x + 8y
(0, 0)	0	0
(760, 0)	6840	6080
(600, 200)	6600	6400
(0, 500)	3000	4000

b) Max profit: 750 aliens and 0 bears
c) Max profit: 600 aliens and 200 bears

Consolidation questions 1

1 a)

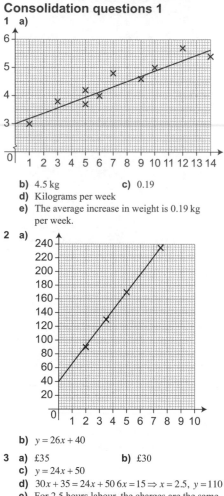

b) 4.5 kg   **c)** 0.19
d) Kilograms per week
e) The average increase in weight is 0.19 kg per week.

2 a)

b) $y = 26x + 40$

3 a) £35   **b)** £30
c) $y = 24x + 50$
d) $30x + 35 = 24x + 50$ $6x = 15 \Rightarrow x = 2.5$, $y = 110$
e) For 2.5 hours labour, the charges are the same (£110)

4 a) Line should pass through (0, 65.2) and (3276, 0)
b) −0.0199 [or −0.02]   **c)** 36.3
d) Max fuel consumption is 65.2 [or equivalent]

Chapter 2
Preparation
1 a) $x^2 + 8x + 12$ **b)** $x^2 + 5x - 36$
c) $x^2 - 25$ **d)** $x^2 - 9x + 8$
e) $x^2 - 6x + 9$ **f)** $12x^2 - 17x - 5$

2 a) $3(x - 2)$ **b)** $x(x + 9)$ **c)** $2x(2x - 5)$

3 a) $x^2 - 8x + 16 + 5x - 6 = x^2 - 3x + 10$
b) $8(x^2 + 6x + 9) - 27 = 8x^2 + 48x + 45$
c) $-(x^2 - 14x + 49) + 31 = -x^2 + 14x - 18$
d) $2x^2 - 11x - 21 + 3x + 9 = 2x^2 - 8x - 12$

4 7, (1), −1, 1, 7

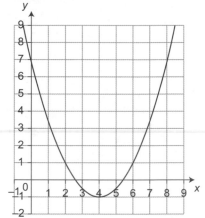

Exercise 2.1

1 a) $4x^2 - 25$ **b)** $49x^2 - 9y^2$
c) $16x^2 + 40x + 25$ **d)** $100q^2 - 60q + 9$
e) $40x^2 - 96x$ **f)** $3y^3 + 9y^2$
g) $-4x(x^2 + 12x + 36) = -4x^3 - 48x^2 - 144x$
h) $x(x^2 - 9) = x^3 - 9x$
i) $T(T^2 + 2T - 35) = T^3 + 2T^2 - 35T$

2 a) $(x + 4)(x + 7)$ **b)** $(T - 4)(T + 3)$
c) $(x - 8)(x + 3)$ **d)** $(x + 8)(x - 3)$
e) $(y - 5)(y - 6)$ **f)** $2x(3x + 2)$
g) $x^2(x - 1)$ **h)** $(t - 8)(t + 8)$
i) $15(x^2 - 16) = 15(x - 4)(x + 4)$
j) $(3v - 2)(3v + 2)$
k) $5(x^2 + 4x + 3) = 5(x + 1)(x + 3)$
l) $x(x^2 - 1) = x(x - 1)(x + 1)$
m) $(w + 6)^2$ **n)** $(2x - 5)^2$
o) $x(3x + 4)^2$ **p)** $(7 - w)(7 + w)$
q) $(5 - x)(3 + x)$ **r)** $(5 - 2x)^2$

3 a) $x = 0$ or 1.5 **b)** $x = -3$ or 0.5
c) $x(x + 5) = 0 \Rightarrow x = 0$ or -5
d) $t(23 - t) = 0 \Rightarrow t = 0$ or 23
e) $(n + 1)(n + 3) = 0 \Rightarrow n = -1$ or -3
f) $(x + 10)(x + 2) = 0 \Rightarrow x = -10$ or -2
g) $(N - 7)(N - 2) = 0 \Rightarrow N = 7$ or 2
h) $(x + 14)(x - 2) = 0 \Rightarrow x = -14$ or 2
i) $(x - 7)(x + 6) = 0 \Rightarrow x = 7$ or -6
j) $(C - 9)(C + 9) = 0 \Rightarrow x = 9$ or -9

k) $6(T^2 - 4) = 0 \Rightarrow 6(T - 2)(T + 2) = 0$
   $\Rightarrow T = 2 \text{ or } -2$
l) $(x + 7)^2 = 0 \Rightarrow x = -7$
m) $(x - 9)^2 = 0 \Rightarrow x = 9$
n) $(2x + 5)^2 = 0 \Rightarrow x = -2.5$
o) $4y^2(y - 3) = 0 \Rightarrow y = 3 \text{ or } 0$
p) $x(x - 1)(x - 3) = 0 \Rightarrow x = 0, 1 \text{ or } 3$

4 a) $x^2 + 5x - 6 = 0 \Rightarrow$
   $(x - 1)(x + 6) = 0 \Rightarrow x = 1 \text{ or } -6$
b) $t^2 - 4t - 12 = 0 \Rightarrow (t - 6)(t + 2) = 0$
   $\Rightarrow t = 6 \text{ or } -2$
c) $x^2 - 8x - 48 = 0 \Rightarrow (x - 12)(x + 4) = 0$
   $\Rightarrow x = 12 \text{ or } -4$
d) $x^2 - 8x + 16 - 5x + 14 = 0 \Rightarrow$
   $x^2 - 13x + 30 = 0 \Rightarrow (x - 10)(x - 3) = 0$
   $\Rightarrow x = 10 \text{ or } 3$
e) $x^2 - 10x + 21 = 0 \Rightarrow (x - 7)(x - 3) = 0$
   $\Rightarrow x = 7 \text{ or } 3$
f) $p^2 + 8p = 9 \Rightarrow p^2 + 8p - 9 = 0$
   $\Rightarrow (p + 9)(p - 1) = 0 \Rightarrow p = 1 \text{ or } -9$

5 a) $0.02x(x - 60) = 0 \text{ so } x = 60$
b) $x = 30$
c) $y = 0.02 \times 30^2 - 1.2 \times 30 = -18$
   Greatest depth = 18 m

6 a) $r = 20$
b) $3x(20 - x) = 252 \Rightarrow 60x - 3x^2 = 252$
   $\Rightarrow 20x - x^2 = 84 \Rightarrow 0 = x^2 - 20x + 84$
c) $(x - 14)(x - 6) = 0 \Rightarrow x = 6 \text{ m or } 14 \text{ m}$

7 Possible results include: **a)** and **c)** have a max value and **b)** has a min value

Exercise 2.2

1 a) $x + 5 = 3 \text{ or } -3 \rightarrow x = -2 \text{ or } -8$
b) $x - 3 = \sqrt{14} \text{ or } -\sqrt{14} \Rightarrow x = 6.74 \text{ or } -0.742$
c) $(x - 5)^2 = 5 \Rightarrow x - 5 = \sqrt{5} \text{ or } -\sqrt{5}$
   $\Rightarrow x = 7.24 \text{ or } 2.76$
d) $(2x + 5)^2 = 17 \Rightarrow 2x + 1 = \sqrt{17} \text{ or } -\sqrt{17} \Rightarrow$
   $x = 1.56 \text{ or } -2.56$

2 a) $(x + 1)^2 - 1$ **b)** $(x - 1.5)^2 - 2.25$
c) $(x - 1)^2 - 1 + 7 = (x - 1)^2 + 6$
d) $(x + 7.5)^2 - 56.25 - 9 = (x + 7.5)^2 - 65.25$

3 a) $(x + 3)^2 - 9 + 8 = 0 \Rightarrow (x + 3)^2 = 1$
   $\Rightarrow x = -2 \text{ or } -4$
b) $(x - 4)^2 - 16 - 10 = 0 \Rightarrow$
   $(x - 4)^2 = 26 \Rightarrow x = 9.10 \text{ or } -1.10$
c) $(x - 6)^2 - 36 = 9 \Rightarrow (x - 6)^2 = 45 \rightarrow$
   $x = 12.7 \text{ or } -0.708$
d) $(x + 3.5)^2 - 12.25 + 5 = 0 \rightarrow$
   $(x + 3.5)^2 = 7.25 \Rightarrow \quad x = -6.19 \text{ or } -0.807$

4 You have to take the square root of a negative number: no solution

5 a) $2(x^2 + 6x) + 7 = 2((x + 3)^2 - 9) + 7$
   $= 2(x + 3)^2 - 11$
b) $5(x^2 - 1.6x) - 4 = 5((x - 0.8)^2 - 0.64) - 4$
   $= 5(x - 0.8)^2 - 7.2$
c) $-(x^2 - 16x) - 9 = -((x - 8)^2 - 64) - 9$
   $= -(x - 8)^2 + 55$

d) $-6(x^2 + 2.167x) + 22$
   $= -6((x + 1.083)^2 - 1.17) + 22$
   $= -6(x + 1.083)^2 + 29.0$

6 a) $2(x^2 + 8) + 3 = 0 \Rightarrow$
   $2((x + 4)^2 - 16) + 3 = 0 \Rightarrow 2(x + 4)^2 = 29$
   $x = -0.192 \text{ or } -7.81$
b) $-(x^2 + 6x) + 21 = 0 \Rightarrow -((x + 3)^2 - 9) + 21 = 0$
   $\Rightarrow (x + 3)^2 = 30 \quad x = 2.48 \text{ or } -8.48$

7 a) i) 9   **ii)** 7   **iii)** min
b) i) -15 **ii)** -2 **iii)** max
c) $(x + 2)^2 - 4$
   i) -4 **ii)** -2 **iii)** min
d) $-((x - 4)^2 - 16) = -(x - 4)^2 + 16$
   i) 16   **ii)** 4   **iii)** max
e) $(x - 9)^2 - 81 - 2$
   i) -83 **ii)** 9   **iii)** min
f) $4((x + 1.5)^2 - 2.25) + 6$
   i) -3 **ii)** -1.5 **iii)** min
g) $-5((x + 1.2)^2 - 1.44) - 3$
   i) 4.2   **ii)** -1.2 **iii)** max

8 $f(x) = (x + 8)^2 + 3 = x^2 + 16x + 67$
   $b - 16, c - 67$

9 a) 13 m   **b)** 5 m
c) $y = 13 - 0.5(5^2) = 0.5$ m

10 $y = 0.5(x + 5)^2 + 1$

11 a) $y = -0.01(x^2 - 70x)$
   $= -0.01((x - 35)^2 - 1225)$
   $= -0.01(x - 35)^2 + 12.25$
b) 12.25 m   **c)** 35 m

12 $\left(x + \dfrac{b}{2a}\right)^2 - \dfrac{b^2}{4a^2} + \dfrac{c}{a} = 0$

$\left(x + \dfrac{b}{2a}\right)^2 = \dfrac{b^2 - 4ac}{4a^2}$

$x + \dfrac{b}{2a} = \dfrac{\sqrt{(b^2 - 4ac)}}{2a} \text{ or } -\dfrac{\sqrt{(b^2 - 4ac)}}{2a}$

$x = \dfrac{-b + \sqrt{(b^2 - 4ac)}}{2a} \text{ or } \dfrac{-b - \sqrt{(b^2 - 4ac)}}{2a}$

Exercise 2.3

1 a) $\Delta = -3$, no real roots
b) $\Delta = 0$, equal roots
c) $\Delta = -191$, no real roots
d) $\Delta = 16$, distinct roots

2 a) $x = 1.47 \text{ or } -7.47$ **b)** $x = 2 \text{ or } \dfrac{1}{3}$
c) $x = -2 \text{ or } 4.5$ **d)** $x = 1.8$
e) no real roots   **f)** $x = 1.57 \text{ or } -9.57$

3 a) $x^2 - 12x + 3 = 0 \quad x = 11.7 \text{ or } 0.255$
b) $5x^2 + 10x - 6 = 0 \quad x = 0.483 \text{ or } -2.48$
c) $2x^2 + 10x + 7 = 0 \quad x = -0.842 \text{ or } -4.16$
d) $-x^2 + 17x - 45 = 0 \quad x = 3.28 \text{ or } 13.7$
e) $7x^2 + 11x - 3 = 0 \quad x = 0.237 \text{ or } -1.81$
f) $0 = 4x^2 + 5x - 12 \quad x = 1.22 \text{ or } -2.47$

4 a) $x^2 + 9x - 14 = 0 \quad x = 1.35 \text{ or } -10.4$
b) $x^2 + 4x - 3 = 0 \quad x = 0.646 \text{ or } -4.65$

5 $0.6x^2 + 2.4x + 1.6 = 0 \quad x = -0.845 \text{ or } -3.15$

6 $4.5817 \text{ m} = 15' \, 0.4"$

7 $0.5q^2 - 8.4q + 22 = 0$; $q = 3.25$; £9.54

8 $14x^2 + x - 1 = 0$; $x = 0.234$

9 $-0.015x^2 + 0.345x - 1.38 = 0$; $x = 17.8$ m

10 a) $x_1 + x_2 = \dfrac{-b + \sqrt{(b^2 - 4ac)} - b - \sqrt{(b^2 - 4ac)}}{2a} = -\dfrac{b}{a}$

b) $\dfrac{1}{2}(x_1 + x_2) = \dfrac{-b}{2a}$

Exercise 2.4

1 a) i) $a > 0, \Delta = 0$ **ii)** min
  iii) ∪-shaped, touches x-axis
  b) i) $a < 0, \Delta < 0$ **ii)** max
  iii) ∩-shaped, below x-axis t
  c) i) $a < 0, \Delta > 0$ **ii)** max
  iii) ∩-shaped, crosses x-axis twice
  d) i) $a > 0, \Delta > 0$ **ii)** min
  iii) ∪-shaped, crosses x-axis twice

2 a) i) $y = 2x(x - 20)$
  ii) $y = 2(x - 10)^2 - 200$
  iii) ∪-shaped, min at $(10, -200)$,
    y-intercept 0, x-intercepts 0 and 20

  b) i) $y = x(100 - x)$
  ii) $y = -(x - 50)^2 + 2500$
  iii) ∩-shaped, max at $(50, 2500)$,
    y-intercept 0, x-intercepts 0 and 100

  c) i) $y = (x + 5)(x + 3)$
  ii) $y = (x + 4)^2 - 1$
  iii) ∪-shaped, min at $(-4, -1)$,
    y-intercept 15, x-intercepts -3 and -5

  d) i) $y = (x - 5)(x + 4)$
  ii) $y = (x - 0.5)^2 - 20.25$
  iii) ∪-shaped, min at $(0.5, 20.25)$,
    y-intercept -20, x-intercepts -4 and 5

3 a) i) $y = (x - 10)^2 - 83$
  ii) $x = 19.1$ and 0.890
  iii) ∪-shaped, min at $(10, -83)$,
    y-intercept 17

  b) i) $y = (x + 4.5)^2 - 26.25$
  ii) $x = 0.623$ and -9.62
  iii) ∪-shaped, min at $(-4.5, -26.25)$,
    y-intercept -6

  c) i) $y = (x + 2)^2 + 8$
  ii) $x = 19.1$ and 0.890
  iii) ∪-shaped, min at $(-2, 8)$, y-intercept 12

  d) i) $y = 4(x - 1.25)^2 - 11.25$
  ii) $x = 2.93$ and -0.427
  iii) ∪-shaped, min at $(1.25, -11.25)$,
    y-intercept -5

  e) i) $y = 0.08(x - 3.75)^2 - 2.325$
  ii) $x = -1.64$ and 9.14
  iii) ∪-shaped, min at $(3.75, -2.325)$,
    y-intercept -1.2

  f) i) $y = -0.62(x - 0.331)^2 + 0.158$
  ii) $x = -0.174$ and 0.835
  iii) ∩-shaped, max at $(0.331, 0.158)$,
    y-intercept 0.09

4 a) i) $x(x + 5)$.
  ii) Min $(-2.5, -6.25)$
  iii) ∪-shaped, y-intercept 0, x-intercepts -5, 0
  b) i) $3x(1 - 20x)$.
  ii) Max $(0.025, 0.0375)$
  iii) ∩-shaped, y-intercept 0, x-intercepts 0, 20
  c) i) $(x - 11)(x - 5)$.
  ii) Min $(8, -9)$
  iii) ∪-shaped, y-intercept 55, x-intercepts 5, 11
  d) i) $(3 - x)(3 + x)$
  ii) Max $(0, 9)$
  iii) ∩-shaped y-intercept 9, x-intercepts -3, 3
  e) i) $(x - 4)(x + 1)$.
  ii) Min $(1.5, -6.25)$
  iii) ∪-shaped, y-intercept -4, x-intercepts -1, 4
  f) i) $(6 - x)(2 + x)$
  ii) Max $(2, 16)$
  iii) ∩-shaped, y-intercept 12, x-intercepts -2, 6

5 a) $(x + 2.5)^2 - 6.25$
  b) $-60(x - 0.025)^2 + 0.0375$
  c) $(x - 8)^2 - 9$ **d)** $-x^2 + 9$
  e) $(x - 1.5)^2 - 6.25$ **f)** $-(x - 2)^2 + 16$

6 a) i) $x = 0.395, 7.61$
  ii) Min $(4, -39)$
  iii) ∪-shaped, y-intercept 9
  b) i) $\Delta < 0$ so no x-intercept
  ii) Min $(-0.75, 3.625)$
  iii) ∪-shaped, y-intercept 7
  c) i) $x = -0.5, 3.5$
  ii) Max $(1.5, 16)$
  iii) ∩-shaped, y-intercept 7
  d) i) $x = 0.661, 6.48$
  ii) Min $(3.75, -5.92)$
  iii) ∪-shaped, y-intercept 3

7 a) ∩-shaped, max $(12.5, 31.25)$
    y-intercept 0 x-intercepts 0, 25
  b) ∪-shaped, min $(0, -9)$ y-intercept -9
    x-intercepts -1.22, 1.22
  c) ∪-shaped, min $(0, 5)$ y-intercept 5
    $\Delta < 0$ so no x-intercepts
  d) ∪-shaped, min $(-4.5, -2.25)$
    y-intercept 18 x-intercepts -6, -3
  e) ∪-shaped, min $(2.33, 0)$
    y-intercept 49 x-intercepts 2.33 (double root)
  f) ∪-shaped, min $(-0.25, -11.375)$
    y-intercept -11 x-intercepts -1.63, 1.13
  g) ∩-shaped, max $(0.625, -5.4375)$
    y-intercept -7 $\Delta < 0$ so no x-intercepts
  h) ∩-shaped, max $(-2.7, 7.95)$
    y-intercept 4.3 x-intercepts -6.69, 1.29, 0

8 a) 1.2 m **b)** 5.15 m **c)** max (1.8, 1.69)

9 Min $(2.2, -0.016)$; $(0, 1.92)$; $(2, 0)$, $(2.4, 0)$

10 ∩-shaped, max $(11.5, 2.90)$, end points
  $(0, 0.92)$; $(25.4, 2.3)$

Exercise 2.5

1 a) B **b)** C **c)** F **d)** D
  e) H **f)** I **g)** k **h)** E
  i) J **j)** G **k)** A

2

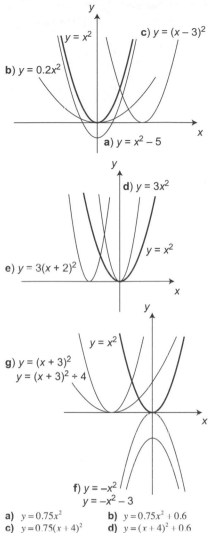

b) $y = 0.2x^2$

$y = x^2$

c) $y = (x-3)^2$

a) $y = x^2 - 5$

d) $y = 3x^2$

$y = x^2$

e) $y = 3(x+2)^2$

$y = x^2$

g) $y = (x+3)^2$
$y = (x+3)^2 \div 4$

f) $y = -x^2$
$y = -x^2 - 3$

3 **a)** $y = 0.75x^2$ **b)** $y = 0.75x^2 + 0.6$
   c) $y = 0.75(x+4)^2$ **d)** $y = (x+4)^2 + 0.6$

4 **a)** Translate 10 to the right
   b) Invert (turn upside down), make 4 times as steep
   c) Translate down 1
   d) Invert, translate 1.5 to the left
   e) Half as steep, 2 to the left
   f) 6 times as steep, down 1
   g) 3 times as steep, 2 to the right, up 9

5 $y = 14.5 - 0.5(x-5)^2$

6 $y = 0.6(x-5)^2 - 0.45$

Investigation 2

1   Computer Aided Design (CAD) systems, computer graphics, typography, etc.

Consolidation questions 2

1 $(\pm 40, 67.4)$, $(\pm 30, 59.8)$, $(\pm 20, 54.3)$, $(\pm 10, 51.1)$, $(0, 50)$
   b) 50 m   **c)** 65.7 m
     Stretch parallel to y axis, SF $= \dfrac{1}{92}$
     y translation 50 or $\begin{pmatrix} 0 \\ 50 \end{pmatrix}$

2   **a)** 0, 71, 115, 133, 123, 87, 24, 0
   b) 5 plots to $\frac{1}{2}$ square accuracy, smooth correct curve through points
   c) 75 to 80 and 233 to 239
   d) 7 to nearest integer
   e) $A = 133$ to nearest integer
     $B = 157.5$ or 158
   f) $A = $ max height or max y-value
     $B = $ value of x at max height

3   **a)** 5 correct plots e.g. $(0, 0)$ $(5, 75)$ $(10, 100)$ $(15, 75)$ $(20, 0)$
   b) 100; $t = 10$ **c)** 20
   d) i) $q = 10, p = 100$
     ii) $q = $ value of t at max $p = $ max number of tickets sold

4   **a)** It gives a negative value
   b) 7 correct values e.g. $(0, 0)$ $(5, 625)$ $(10, 1000)$ $(15, 1125)$ $(20, 1000)$ $(25, 625)$ $(30, 0)$
   c) i) 1125   **ii)** 15
   d) $q = 15, p = 1125$
   e) $q = $ value of x, $p = $ income
   f) 23.1, 6.94

5   **a) i)** $9.6 - 9.8$ **ii)** $24 - 26$
   b) $10\sqrt{15}$ or 22.36
   c) The values always decrease, becoming negative, which is unrealistic.

6   **a)**

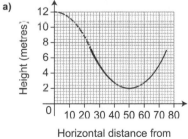

Horizontal distance from start (metres)

   b) 2 (at $x = 50$)
   c) The values always increase, without limit, which is unrealistic.

Chapter 3
Preparation

1   **a)** 0.906   **b)** 0   **c)** 0.139
2   **a)** 24.8°   **b)** 31.8°
3   **a)** 36.9°   **b)** 73.1°

Exercise 3.1

1 Positive: **a c d f k l o p**,
Negative: **b e h l m n**, Zero: **g j**

2 **a)** $\pm\{90°, 270°, 450°, 630°, 810°, 990°\}$
b) $\pm\{0°, 180°, 360°, 540°, 720°, 900°\}$
c) $-990°, -630°, -270°, 90°, 450°, 810°$
d) $\pm\{180°, 540°, 900°\}$

3 **a)** $47.9°, 312.1°$ **b)** $62.8°, 117.1°$
c) $97.5°, 262.5°$ **d)** $205.5°, 334.5°$
e) $\cos\theta = -0.64$; $129.8°, 230.2°$
f) $\sin\theta = -0.993$; $291.0°, 249.0°$

4 **a)** $-16.3°, -163.7°$ **b)** $33.9°, -33.9°, 326.1°$
c) $\sin\theta = 0.75$; $48.6°$
d) $\cos\theta = 0.64$; $50.2°, 309.8°, -50.2°, -309.8°$

5 **a)** cosine graph **b)** sine graph
c) circle

Exercise 3.2

1 **a)** A **b)** E **c)** H **d)** D
e) J **f)** F **g)** C **h)** B
i) I **j)** G

2 **a)** **i)** 10 **ii)** 0 **iii)** 10
iv) -10 **v)** 360 **vi)** $\dfrac{1}{360}$

b) **i)** 12 **ii)** 0 **iii)** 12
iv) -12 **v)** 12 **vi)** $\dfrac{1}{12}$

c) **i)** 8 **ii)** 17 **iii)** 25
iv) 9 **v)** 360 **vi)** $\dfrac{1}{360}$

d) **i)** 3 **ii)** -1 **iii)** 2
iv) -4 **v)** 6 **vi)** $\dfrac{1}{6}$

e) **i)** 5 **ii)** 3 **iii)** 8
iv) -2 **v)** 0.36 **vi)** $\dfrac{100}{36} = \dfrac{25}{9}$

f) **i)** 80 **ii)** 0 **iii)** 80
iv) -80 **v)** 90 **vi)** $\dfrac{1}{90}$

3 **a)** $y = 12\sin t°$ **b)** $y = 7\sin(4t)°$
c) $y = 5\sin(0.5t)°$ **d)** $y = 4\sin(6t)° + 2$
e) $y = 10\sin(4(t-30))°$
f) $y = 4\sin(t+20)°$

4 Check on shape computer/calculator

a) max (90, 8); min (270, −8)
b) max (0, 6), (360, 6); min (180, −6)
c) max (18, 1); min (54, −1)
d) max (0, 1), (4, 1); min (2, −1)
e) max (0, −2), (360, −2); min (180, −4)
f) max (90, 13); min (270, −3)
g) max (30, 12); min (90, −12)
h) max (0, 2.5), (36, 2.5); min (18, 1.5)
i) max (110, 3); min (290, −3)
j) min (15, −2); max (60, 2)

5 **a)** Vertical stretch, SF = 8
b) Translation $\begin{pmatrix} 0 \\ -0.5 \end{pmatrix}$ **c)** Translation $\begin{pmatrix} 90° \\ 0 \end{pmatrix}$
d) Translation $\begin{pmatrix} -50 \\ 0 \end{pmatrix}$
e) Horizontal stretch, SF = 1/3;
Translation $\begin{pmatrix} -50 \\ 0 \end{pmatrix}$
f) Horizontal stretch, SF = 1/3;
Translation $\begin{pmatrix} -50 \\ 0 \end{pmatrix}$;
Vertical stretch, SF = 1/2
g) Translation $\begin{pmatrix} 90° \\ 0 \end{pmatrix}$
h) Horizontal stretch, SF = 1/3;
Translation $\begin{pmatrix} -50 \\ 0 \end{pmatrix}$;
Vertical stretch, SF = 1/2;
Translation $\begin{pmatrix} 0 \\ 1.2 \end{pmatrix}$

6 **a)** $30°, 150°$ **a)** $180°, 540°$
c) $99.3°, 140.7°$ **d)** $28.1°, 91.9°$

7 **a)** $y = 4\sin x°$ **b)** $y = 4\sin x° - 2$
c) $y = \sin(x+90)°$, same as cos

8 **a)** $y = \cos(5x)°$ **b)** $y = 2\cos(5x)°$
c) $y = 2\cos(5x)° + 3$
d) $y = 3\cos(4(x-20))° - 7$

9 **a)** $a = 0.1$, $k = 18\,000$ **b)** 0.1 m
c) 2.47×10^{-3} s **d)** $y = 0.1\sin(27\,000t)°$

10 A sine or cosine function.

Investigation 3

1 Electronics, music sampling, image processing, etc.

2 Period = 12:15 − 12:50 hrs
High tide = 3.9 − 4.6 m
Low tide = 0.9 − 1.6 m
Amplitude = 2.3 − 3.7 m
Central value = 2.65 − 2.85 m

3 $\odot : M = 1.99 \times 10^{30}$ kg, $R = 1.50 \times 10^{11}$ m
$\mathbb{C} : M = 7.35 \times 10^{22}$ kg, $R = 3.84 \times 10^8$ m
F_G $\odot : \mathbb{C} = 1 : 0.0056$
F_T $\odot : \mathbb{C} = 1 : 2.20$

4 Use sidereal orbital periods:
$T_{\mathbb{C}} = 27.321582$ days
$T_{\oplus} = 0.9972699$ days
$$\frac{1}{2} + \frac{t}{T_{\mathbb{C}}} = \frac{t}{T_{\oplus}}$$
$t = 0.51752523$ days = 12 hr 25' 14"

Consolidation questions 3

1 **a)** (10, 17.2) (12, 13.7) (14, 8.31) (16, 3.57)
(18, 1.7) (20, 3.57)
b) **i)** 17.7 **ii)** 9
c) **i)** Tangent drawn at t = 7 Gradient = 1.6 to 2
ii) m/s or ms^{-1}
iii) Rate of change of height (how quickly "you" are going up)
d) **i)** Amplitude = 8 **ii)** Period = 18
e) **i)** 4.5; 22.5 or 13.5
ii) $(t = 0)$ $h = 1.7$ m, $(t = 9)$ $h = 17.7$ m

2 a) $(0, -42)$ $(13, -12)$ $(26, 18)$ $(39, -12)$
$(52, -42)$ 5 correct values correct plots to ½ sq accuracy Smooth, correct shape curve
b) 19.1 to 19.3   **c)** 13
d) i) Translation $\begin{pmatrix} 0 \\ -12 \end{pmatrix}$
  ii) Stretch (along) T or y axis SF $= 30$

3 a) i) 5.85 to 5.95
  ii) 6.8 to 7.0; and 11 to 11.2
  iii) Tangent drawn at $t = 4$; -0.5 to -0.6
  iv) metres/hour
  v) At 4 a.m. the tide is falling at 0.6 metres per hour
b) Stretch in x-direction, SF $= 1/30$
Stretch in y-direction, SF $= 2.2$
Translation $\begin{pmatrix} 0 \\ 4 \end{pmatrix}$
c) Max too big or min too small

4 a) i) 19, 16.5, 19, 21.5, 19
  ii) 5 plots to ½ square accuracy, smooth, correct shape curve
  iii) 16.30   **iv)** 21.30

Chapter 4
Preparation
1 a) 17 956   **b)** 1.98×10^9
c) 9.77×10^{-4} **d)** 1.28   **e)** 0.187
f) 4.48   **g)** 3.76   **h)** -1

2 a) 225   **b)** 216   **c)** 128   **d)** 243

3 a) 10   **b)** 12   **c)** 4   **d)** 3

4 a) $\frac{1}{8}$ **b)** 5

5 a) 58.1   **b)** 3.09×10^{-3}

6 a) $y = 2tr$ **b)** $y = \frac{a}{s}$

c) $y = \frac{3a}{4v}$ **d)** $y = \pm\sqrt{\left(\frac{4\pi}{x}\right)}$

7 a) 2.3×10^6 **b)** 4.5×10^{-10}

8 a) 0.0000689   **b)** 41000000

Exercise 4.1
1 a) 3^9 **b)** 3^5 **c)** 3^{74}

d) 3^9 **e)** 3^{-6} **f)** $3^{\frac{1}{6}}$

g) $3^{\frac{1}{2}}$ **h)** 3^5 **i)** $3^{3.5}$
j) 3^{10}

2 a) 512   **b)** 500   **c)** 1

d) $\frac{1}{216}$ **e)** 5   **f)** 4

g) 8   **h)** 49   **i)** $\frac{1}{243}$
j) 2

3 a) 282 475 249   **b)** 2.605 **c)** 0.0521

4 a) t^{11} **b)** y **c)** y^{15}

d) t^{-2} **e)** a^2 **f)** $s^{20} t^{15}$

g) $6b^3$ **h)** a^4 **i)** $y^{\frac{2}{3}}$ **j)** t^5

5 a) $\sqrt[3]{(-91)} = -4.50$ **b)** $25^{\frac{3}{2}} = 125$

c) $0.012^{-\frac{1}{5}} = 2.42$

6 $11.86^{\frac{2}{3}} = 5.20$ AU

7 a) Each step up a note the frequency is multiplied by r. C' is 12 notes higher than C, so
$261.6r^{12} = 523.2$

b) $r^{12} = 2 \Rightarrow r = 2^{\frac{1}{12}} = 1.0595$
c) $261.6 \times 1.0595 = 277.2$
d) $261.6 \times 1.0595^7 = 392.0$

Exercise 4.2
1 $24 \div 5 = 4.8$ days

2 $k = 210$
a) $210 \div 8 = 26.25$ **b)** $210 \div 13.5 = 15.6$

3 $k = 1.2 \times 20^2 = 480$
a) $480 \div 9 = 53.3$ **b)** $480 \div 30 = 16$, $\sqrt{16} = 4$

4 $308 \div 30 = 10.3$ days

5 a) $k = 45 \times 2\frac{2}{3} = 120$
$T = \dfrac{120}{v}$
b) the distance

6 $k = 3000 \Rightarrow R = \dfrac{3000}{d^2}$
a) 750μ Sv   **b)** $\sqrt{15} = 3.87$ m

7 $k = 45600$
a) 3260 pascals   **b)** 8.77 L

8 $k = 10.08$
a) $8.23 \times 10^{-3}\ \dfrac{\text{w}}{\text{m}^2}$ **b)** $d = \sqrt{1008} = 31.7$ m

Exercise 4.3
1 a) E **b)** B   **c)** F   **d)** D
  e) A   **f)** C

2 $k \cong 6.1 \times 10^{-3}$

3 $k \cong 4.0 \times 10^{14}$

4 $T = 2.0l^{0.5}$

5 Because x^2 is always positive.
Even powers of x are even functions and odd powers of x are odd functions.

Exercise 4.4
1 a) $\log_{10} 0.0001 = -4$ **b)** $\log_2 128 = 7$

c) $\log_{16} 2 = \dfrac{1}{4}$ **d)** $\log_{36}\left(\dfrac{1}{6}\right) = -0.5$

2 a) $10^4 = 10000$ **b)** $9^{0.5} = 3$

c) $4^{4.5} = 512$ **d)** $7^{-2} = \dfrac{1}{49}$

3 a) 6   **b)** 5   **c)** -3
d) 4   **e)** 0   **f)** 1
g) -1 **h)** -3 **i)** 0.5

4 a) 4.32   **b)** 0.32 **c)** $-3 + 0.32 = -2.68$

5 a) 6.89 **b)** 0.89 **c)** $-2 + 0.89 = -1.11$

6 If the number has n digits, the log is between n and $n-1$

7 If there are n zeros after the decimal point, the log is between $-n$ and $-n-1$

8 $27 = 9^{1.5} \Rightarrow \log_9 27 = 1.5$

9 $8 = 0.5^{-3} \Rightarrow \log_{0.5} 8 = -3$

10 a) 65.1dB **b)** 2.51×10^{-4}

11 a) $10^{9.2} \times (1 \times 10^{-12}) = 1.58 \times 10^{-3}$

b) $k = 0.12838 \Rightarrow I = 1.43 \times 10^{-4}$
c) 81.5 dB; there are enough speakers

12 a) 5.34, acidic

b) $10^{-3.5} = 3.16 \times 10^{-4}$

13 $2.1 = -2.5\log_{10}\left(\dfrac{3 \times 10^{-9}}{I_2}\right)$

$\dfrac{3 \times 10^{-9}}{I_2} = 10^{-0.84} = 0.145$

$I_2 = 2.08 \times 10^{-8}$

Exercise 4.5

1 a) $\log 4$ **b)** $\log 36$ **c)** $\log 81$
d) $\log 5$ **e)** $\log 6$ **f)** $\log(3xy^4)$

2 a) 0.954 **b)** 0.903

c) $\log_{10}\left(\dfrac{3 \times 10}{2}\right) = 1.176$

3 a) 18 **b)** 13
c) 14 **d)** 4

4 a) $\log 2$ **b)** $7\log x$
c) $-2\log x$ **d)** 0

5 a) 6 **b)** $\dfrac{1}{7}$ **c)** 16

6 a) $3\log x + \log y$ **b)** $\log x + \log y - \log z$

c) $\log z + \dfrac{1}{2}\log y$ **d)** $3\log y + \log x$

e) $3\log x - \dfrac{1}{2}\log z$ **f)** 0

7 a) $\log_{10} y = \log_{10} 5 + \log_{10} x$
b) $\log_{10} y = 8\log_{10} x$
c) $\log_{10} y = \log_{10} 6 + 2\log_{10} x$
d) $\log_{10} y = 5\log_{10} x - \log_{10} 3$
e) $\log_{10} y = \log_{10} 18 - 4\log_{10} x$
f) $\log_{10} y = \log_{10} 3 + \dfrac{1}{2}\log_{10} x$

8 $\log_{10} N = \log_{10} k + m\log_{10} t$

9 $\log_{10} y = \log_{10} k + t\log_{10} a$

10 Use the same definitions of x and y.
2nd law: Find $^x/_y$, use the 2nd law of indices and take logs
3rd law: Find x^n, use the 3rd law of indices and take logs

Investigation 4

1 C to C′ $\Rightarrow$ C′ $= 1 \times 2 = 2$

C to G $\Rightarrow$ G $= 1 \times \dfrac{3}{2} = \dfrac{3}{2}$

C′ to F $\Rightarrow$ F $= 2 \div \dfrac{3}{2} = \dfrac{4}{3}$

G to D′ to D $\Rightarrow$ D $= \dfrac{3}{2} \times \dfrac{3}{2} \div 2 = \dfrac{9}{8}$

D to A $\Rightarrow$ A $= \dfrac{9}{8} \times \dfrac{3}{2} = \dfrac{27}{16}$

A to E′ to E $\Rightarrow$ E $= \dfrac{27}{16} \times \dfrac{3}{2} \div 2 = \dfrac{81}{64}$

E to B $\Rightarrow$ A $= \dfrac{81}{64} \times \dfrac{3}{2} = \dfrac{243}{128}$

2 1.25%

3 -0.113%

4 For example, 12 note ET
$3:2$ C : G -0.113%
$4:3$ C : F 0.113%
$5:4$ C : E 0.794%
$9:8$ C : D -0.226%
$5:3$ C : A 0.908%

5 Romanesco brocoli, blood vessels, river systems, lightning bolts, clouds, etc.

6 Cantor set: $\log 2 \div \log 3 = 0.631$
Sierpinski triangle: $\log 3 \div \log 2 = 1.585$
Fractal pyramid: $\log 5 \div \log 2 = 2.322$
Menger sponge: $\log 22 \div \log 3 = 2.727$

Consolidation questions 4

1 a) $k = 2750$
b) $1.375, 2590, 0.887, 3620$
c) Points must be connected by a smooth curve.
2 a) $0.244, 0.615, 1.88, 5.20, 19.2, 30.1$
b) Points must be connected by a smooth curve.
3 a) $466.1 = 261.6 \times (1.05946)^n$
b) $\log 466.1 = \log 261.6 + n\log 1.05946$
so $n = 10$
c) A$\sharp$ or B$\flat$
4 a) $l = 8x^{-2}$ or $l = \dfrac{8}{x^2}$

b) $0.02, 0.0889, 0.005, 0.0032$
c) $109, 103, 99.5, 97.0, 95.1$
d) Points must be connected by a smooth curve.
e) $l = 10^{-3}$ so $x^2 = 8000$ and $x = 89.4\text{m}$

Chapter 5

Preparation

1 a) 2.72 **b)** 0.0498

c) $220\,000$ **d)** 1.0047

2 a) 1.39 **b)** 0

c) -2.30 **d)** 1

3 Graphs of $y =$
a) $-\sqrt{x}$ **b)** $\sqrt{(-x)}$ **c)** x^2

Exercise 5.1

1 a) 4.05   **b)** 3.88   **c)** 34.1

2 a) 8.41   **b)** 71.5   **c)** 8.10

3 a) 0.921   **b)** 2.38   **c)** 72.2

4 a) £13000   **b)** 2.5%
   c) £15452.91   **d)** 3.00 years

5 a) $y = 2000\left(1.18^t\right)$
   b) 4212   **c)** 6.64 hours

6 a) 0.047   **b)** 88.9 days
   c) $a = 0.992$

Exercise 5.2

1 a) $f^{-1}(x) = \dfrac{1}{2}\ln x$ **b)** $f^{-1}(x) = \sqrt{3x}$

   c) $f^{-1}(x) = 4 - x$ **d)** $f^{-1}(x) = e^x + 3$

   e) $f^{-1}(x) = \sqrt[3]{x}$ **f)** $f^{-1}(x) = e^{\frac{x}{4}}$

   g) $f^{-1}(x) = x^2 + 1$ **h)** $f^{-1}(x) = \dfrac{1}{3}\sin^{-1}x$

Exercise 5.3

1 a) I   **b)** C   **c)** A   **d)** G
   e) E   **f)** F   **g)** B   **h)** D
   i) H

2 a, b) Q.5: y keeps increasing; passes through
     (12:00, 2000) and (18:38, 6000)
     Q.6: $y \to 0$; passes through (0, 0.06)
     and (30, 0.048)
   c) Q.5: gradient keeps increasing
     Q.6: gradient $\to 0$

3 asymptotes:
   a) $y = 0$ (the x-axis), $x = 0$ (the y-axis)
   b) $y = 0$ (the x-axis), $x = 0$ (the y-axis)
   c) $y = 0$, $x = 2$ **d)** $y = 3$, $x = 0$
   e) $y = 5$, $x = 4$ **f)** $x = 3$, $y = 0$.

4 a) $f^{-1}(x) = x^2 + 2$
   b) y-axis intercept (0, 2)

5 a) $f^{-1}(x) = -2\ln\dfrac{x}{4}$
   b) x-axis intercept (4,0)

6 a) 195   **b)** 92.6 °C
   c) 18.4 minutes   **d)** It tends to 20 °C
   e) Axis intercept (0, 195), asymptote $y = 20$

7 a) Intercept (0, 0), asymptote $x = -1$
   b) Intercept (e^2, 0), asymptote y-axis
   c) Intercepts (ln 2, 0) and (0, −2),
     asymptote $y = -2$
   d) Intercept (0, −1) and (−0.288 0),
     asymptote $y = -4$

8 a) 200   **b)** 0.139
   c) 4222   **d)** –

9 a) 11890, 13420, 14190
   b, c) $N \to 15000$
   d) 630 [550 – 700 ok]
   e) Bats per year
   f) After 7 years the number of bats was
     increasing by 630 per year
   g) It tends to zero

10 a) i) 289 or 290, 359, 385
     ii) 5 correct plots
   b) 50 or 50.1
   c) 4.3   **d)** 400

Exercise 5.4

1 a) 900, 1600, 2500, 3600, 4900
   b) –
   c) $a = 0.019, b = 6$
   d) 28.3 m   **e)** 53.8 mph

2 a) $\ln y = \ln 200 + t \ln a$
   b) 5.30, 5.07, 4.86, 4.65, 4.48, 4.26
   d) $\ln a \approx -0.20 \Rightarrow a = 0.82$
   e) 47.8 g   **f)** 10.2 days

3 a) $\ln N = \ln k + \ln(t^c)$ $\ln N = \ln k + c \ln t$
   b) 0, 0.693. 1.10, 1.39, 1.61, 1.79:
     4.25, 5.97, 7.00, 7.71, 8.27, 8.73
   c) Correct plots
   d) $\ln k = 4.2$ to 4.3, $c = 2.4$ to 2.6 and
     $\ln N = \ln k + c \ln t$
   e) $k - 66$ to 74, $N - kt^c$

4 a) 100, 1444, 3025, 4624, 6561, 8836
   b) 6 correct plots
   c) 460 to 500
   d) $x^2 = 1700$ to1900; 41 to 44

Investigation 5

1 Exponentials: populations, epidemiology,
radioactive decay, chain reactions, etc.
Logarithms. spiral shells, flight paths, sensory
perception, etc.

2 Any data listed by 'size'/frequency

3 $\ln y = \ln(ab^x) = \ln a + \ln b^x = \ln a + x\ln b$
$y = e^{\ln a + x\ln b} = e^{\ln a}e^{x\ln b} = ae^{x\ln b}$

Consolidation questions 5

1 a) i) y-intercept (0, 100), asymptote $y = 20$
     ii) k = 0.075
   b) i) 15   **ii)** 95   **iii)** 44.4 °C

2 a) i) 1876
     ii) 2017 or 2018, must be an integer
   b) i) 2389
     ii) 2011 or 2012
     iii) Predictions are too low
   c) Graph Q; because it doesn't start at 0 / because
     its y-intercept is 300.

3 **a)** **i)** 22.6   **ii)** 45.8
   b) Gives negative life expectancy
   c) **i)** Sketch
     ii) It is infinite when $x = 0$ (at birth)

4 **a)** 8.16 or 8.2, 11.8, 15.5, 18.2, 19.8
   b) 5 correct plots to $\frac{1}{2}$ sq accuracy on ft
   c) $\ln S = \ln k + t \ln a$
     $\ln k = 8.1$ to 8.6; $\ln a = 0.3$ to 0.35
   d) $a = 1.35$ to 1.42 $k = 3294$ to 5432

5 **a)** $\ln E = \ln k + \ln\left(a^r\right)$
   b) 18.7, 22.2, 25.6, 29.1, 32.5, 35.9 or 36 or 36.0
   c **i)** 6 correct plots to ½ square accuracy
     Line of best fit, need not cross axes, at
     least 15 cm long
     ii) $a = 30.5$ to 33.1; $k = 3.3$ to 5.4
   d) 4.2×10^{21} **e)** 0.6 to 0.7

Practice paper 1

1 **a)** $P = -\left(x^2 - 130x\right) - 3000$
       $= -\left((x - 65)^2 - 4225\right) - 3000$
       $= -(x - 65)^2 + 1225$
   b) £1225   **c)** 65
   d) $(x - 65)^2 = 1225 \Rightarrow x = 100$ or 30

2 **a)** $m = -52, n = 1620; P = -x^2 + 104x - 1084$
   b) 1476   **c)** $x = 27$ or 77

3 **a)** $A = 0.3, c = 37.0, k = 15$
   b) 37.08°
   c) $t = 8.8$ or 15.2
   d) $y = 0.3\cos\left(15(t + 6)\right)° + 37$ or
     $y = 0.3\cos\left(15(t - 18)\right)° + 37$ or
     $y = 0.3\sin(15t)° + 37$

4 **a)** $\ln m = \ln k + c \ln d$
   b) 0.69, 0.956, 1.34, 1.65, 2.19
     0.83, 1.48, 2.40, 3.22, 4.54
   d) $c \approx 2.5$; $\ln k \approx -0.90 \Rightarrow k = 0.41$
     $m = 0.41d^{2.5}$
   e) 197 g   **f)** 6.44 cm

Practice paper 2

1 **a)** $y = 0 \Rightarrow 0.3x(3 - x) = 0$ so $x = 3$.
   b)

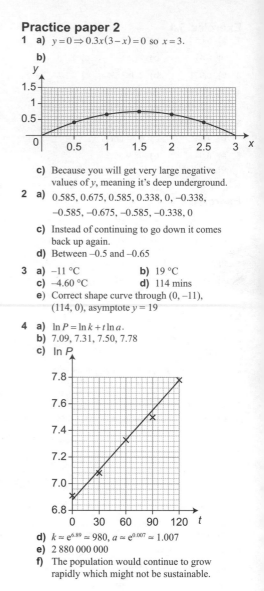

   c) Because you will get very large negative
     values of y, meaning it's deep underground.

2 **a)** 0.585, 0.675, 0.585, 0.338, 0, –0.338,
     –0.585, –0.675, –0.585, –0.338, 0
   c) Instead of continuing to go down it comes
     back up again.
   d) Between –0.5 and –0.65

3 **a)** –11 °C   **b)** 19 °C
   c) –4.60 °C   **d)** 114 mins
   e) Correct shape curve through (0, –11),
     (114, 0), asymptote $y = 19$

4 **a)** $\ln P = \ln k + t \ln a$.
   b) 7.09, 7.31, 7.50, 7.78
   c)
   d) $k \approx e^{6.89} \approx 980$, $a \approx e^{0.007} \approx 1.007$
   e) 2 880 000 000
   f) The population would continue to grow
     rapidly which might not be sustainable.